S0-CAA-760

THE COMMON
TERN

HAMLYN SPECIES GUIDES

THE COMMON TERN

Rob Hume

HAMLYN

COVER ILLUSTRATION *A Common Tern arrives with a fish to feed to its full-grown chick.*

Published in 1993 by Hamlyn,
part of Reed Illustrated Books Limited,
Michelin House, 81 Fulham Road, London SW3 6RB

Text © Rob Hume 1993
Colour illustrations © Norman Arlott 1993
Black-and-white illustrations © Rob Hume 1993
Maps © Reed Illustrated Books 1993

The author's moral rights have been asserted.

The photographs have been reproduced by permission of the following:
pp 18, 19, 23, 34, 35, 50, 59, 122 C.H. Gomersall/RSPB, © RSPB;
pp 14, 15, 26, 46, 58, 66, 70, 71, 87, 102, 106, 110 © Roger Tidman.

All rights reserved. Apart from any fair dealing for the purpose of private study, research, criticism or review, as permitted under the Copyright Designs and Patents Act, 1988, no part of this publication may be reproduced, stored in a retrieval system, or transmitted in any form or by any means, electronic, electrical, chemical, mechanical, optical, photocopying, recording, or otherwise, without prior written permission. All enquiries should be addressed to the Publishers.

British Library Cataloguing in Publication Data

Hume, Rob
  Common Tern. – (Hamlyn Species Guides)
  I. Title II. Arlott, Norman III. Series
  598.3

ISBN 0-540-01266-1

Series Editor David A. Christie
Page design by Jessica Caws
Map by Louise Griffiths
Printed in Hong Kong

CONTENTS

THE SUMMER BREEDING RANGE OF THE COMMON TERN IN THE WESTERN PALEARCTIC

KAZAKHSTAN
CASPIAN SEA
IRAN
IRAQ
KUWAIT
RED SEA
RUSSIA
BARENTS SEA
WHITE SEA
KARA SEA
FINLAND
ESTONIA
LATVIA
LITH.
BELORUSSIA
UKRAINE
GEORGIA
ARM.
AZER.
BLACK SEA
ROMANIA
BULGARIA
TURKEY
ISRAEL
JORDAN
EGYPT
MEDITERRANEAN
GREECE
ALB.
ITALY
TUNISIA
Sardinia
HUNG.
SL.
CZ.
POLAND
RUSSIA
N.
GERMANY
BEL.
DENMARK
NORTH SEA
SWEDEN
NORWAY
FRANCE
S.
SPAIN
IRELAND
UK.
NORTH ATLANTIC
Azores
Madeira
MAURITANIA

KEY

ALB.	ALBANIA
ARM.	ARMENIA
AZER.	AZERBAIJAN
BEL.	BELGIUM
CZ.	CZECH REPUBLIC
LITH.	LITHUANIA
N.	NETHERLANDS
S.	SWITZERLAND
SL.	SLOVAK REPUBLIC
UK.	UNITED KINGDOM

Boundary of
Western Palearctic

Breeding range
of Common Tern

Series Editor's Foreword

THAT master of the air, the Common Tern, is fundamentally, as Rob Hume so succinctly demonstrates, a seabird. Yet it is also well known to many people who rarely visit the coastal waters of Britain and Europe, for it nests not only on extensive marshes or undisturbed beaches around our coasts but also as far inland as one can get. The huge increase in the number of gravel pits in recent decades has benefited this graceful relative of the gulls, which can now be seen breeding close to town centres or flying over busy main roads carrying fish to feed to its young. For a seabird, it has adapted remarkably well to man-made inland habitats, and this alone makes it a subject of special interest for many people, enthusiastic birdwatchers and interested onlookers alike.

A very similar species, the Arctic Tern, also passes through inland areas on its way to coastal breeding sites in the north. Well into the 1970s it was normal for these two species to be referred to as 'commic terns' when it was not certain exactly which of the two was concerned. Rob Hume was one of the very first ornithologists to show that this uncertainty was unnecessary: he pointed out that the two species could be separated quite easily, even at a fair range and in relatively poor light, by differences in the pattern of the outer wing, a feature which is now taken as common knowledge by the birdwatchers of the 1990s (even though, regrettably, the phrase 'commic tern' still persists in some quarters).

Rob's genuine fondness for and knowledge of terns are well known among ornithologists, and he shows in this book just why it is so easy to be fascinated by these long-distance migrants. The Common Tern is here presented as a real living creature rather than simply a subject for scientific study, and the reader will thereby gain a true insight into the life of this highly aerial bird.

This new series of bird monographs is intended to be scientifically accurate, but at the same time not overburdened with scientific 'jargon' which might so easily put off the keen amateur. Here, again, the author's acknowledged expertise in communicating specialist ornithological data in a language easily understandable by all is a major advantage and gives a tremendous boost to the furtherance of ornithology among the amateur and non-specialist alike.

David A. Christie

1

A WORLD OF
EXTREMES

EARTH, wind and water are the elements of a Common Tern's life. Essentially a seabird, it must, like all birds that live most of their lives at sea, come to land to breed. It must seek solid ground, a safe and secure place to lay its eggs and rear its chicks until they are themselves able to fly. Little else is done on land, apart from resting.

To feed, it needs fish, and to catch fish it must have clear, unpolluted water, into which it can plunge headlong for prey already seen from the air. To locate fish, it has to fly, and to survive, it must migrate thousands of miles. It is as much a bird of the air as a bird of the sea.

The world of the Common Tern is a cocktail of salt spray and blown sand, lines of spindrift drawn across the sea, of barnacle-encrusted rock and oily seaweed in a heaving swell. The bird itself is delicate and lightweight, yet able to withstand a roaring gale above the open ocean.

Common Terns are typical of the sea terns, slender, mostly white and pale grey relatives of the larger, heavier, more lumbering gulls. They are, by comparison with some other terns, successful, adaptable, and less severely constrained within sharply defined ecological limits.

As a species, the Common Tern has a wide distribution and rather loosely defined ecological requirements. It may as easily be seen flying above a flooded gravel pit, or a broad river a hundred or a thousand miles from the sea as over the breaking waves on a beach. Nevertheless, it is closely related to a group of terns collectively called the 'sea terns' and is one of those which are more poetically referred to as 'sea swallows'.

While other species of tern make for restricted environments within well-defined zones, the Common Tern breeds anywhere from the fringe of the Arctic to the tropics, taking in temperate and Mediterranean beaches and vast areas of continental Asia and North America on the way. It generally avoids icy seas and the most exposed capes and is a bird of low coasts with accumulating sand and shingle, decidedly not one of the many seabirds that prefer a sheer cliff in summer.

Most of all, perhaps, the Common Tern is associated in many people's minds with low, sandy islands, broad beaches and shingle ridges, the seaward edge of tall dunes held together by clumps of marram grass, and the adjacent gleaming sea. Terns like sandy estuaries, where bright pennants flutter in the sun and the tap of rigging slapping against the masts of moored yachts, the smell of salt, a swirling tide race and a huge sky add up to everyone's image of the seaside.

Common Terns are frequently to be seen with gulls. Standing beside them, even alongside the small Black-headed Gull, they look low-slung, short-legged, slim and diminutive. The rather long head, sunk into its shoulders, exaggerates the inky-black cap of a spring Common Tern, instantly distinguishing it from the gulls. The dark-hooded gulls have a different appearance, their whole faces dark with a sharply defined hood drawn well down over the chin and throat.

The common 'hooded' gull of Europe, the Black-headed Gull, actually has a dark brown hood and the black of the tern's cap stands out surprisingly well, even at a distance when the brown hoods of the gulls do indeed tend to appear 'black'. The real black of the tern makes the gulls' heads look simply 'dark' by comparison. The jet-black hood of a Mediterranean Gull, or in America a Bonaparte's Gull or a Laughing Gull, does not provide the same contrast of colour, but the different shape is still there, the flatter cap of the tern still instantly distinguishable from the full, rounder hoods of the gulls.

In contrast to the sight of the everyday gulls, an encounter with a tern gives most birdwatchers more of a lift, demanding a second look. Is it its elegance, the romance of its migrations, its extra refinement, that somehow make it a 'better bird', more often one for the notebook? Away from favoured coasts, it is in any case not so familiar, not so easily dismissed. In spring, especially, when it is newly returned from a long winter away, the tern adds particular pleasure, as much a sign of the summer to come as a swallow over a meadow.

For most North American and western European birdwatchers, the Common Tern is looked for in April, a week or two later than the Sandwich Tern but earlier than the Little Tern. Even inland it is an early migrant, pausing briefly at all kinds of inland waters on its way north, or arriving at its inland breeding sites to add its own sharp, peevish calls to those of the gulls.

It is a welcome arrival, although it often comes when the weather is still unpredictable, when stinging showers of rain and hail and biting winds interrupt spells with clear, pale blue skies. It is a time when the weather is yet uncertain, unwilling to leave behind the cold and rough days of late winter yet giving a few clues to impatience for the warmth of the summer to come. The tern, as if eager for the summer itself, arrives early, ready to defy a short spell of cold, rain or gales in its anticipation of more balmy seaside days.

The tern is a livelier, more active creature than the gulls, excitable and always likely to do something more than loaf about for ages. True, well-fed, contented terns in late summer do stand in line and while away the hours, but in general terns are too stressed, too harassed and highly strung to do that for long. They are worth watching, because they are usually up to something.

Norman Arlott.

Action means flight and, more often than not, noise. Common Terns let people know they are there: they scream and screech with peculiarly evocative, if not exactly beautiful, calls. Some of the sounds, especially those that are intended to stir other terns to action, are almost irritating to a human ear, but the overall effect of a mêlée of Common Terns is an appealing one.

Even migrants, perhaps tired after a long flight and ready to sit on a safe buoy or pier, cannot keep still for long and have to get up to circle over some water, or fly head-to-wind, low, looking eagerly for fish. In summer, there is endless entertainment near a tern colony, with all kinds of fights and scraps and sudden panics, displays and courtship rituals to enjoy. The dullest tern is usually fidgety, rarely still for long.

Always suspicious and nervous of predators, Common Terns gang together to drive off mammals and other birds that threaten their eggs or chicks. Not so daring as the Arctic Tern, they still swoop remarkably close to the heads of human intruders who stray too close to their nests. It is just the way they are, the way they are programmed, yet it would be easy to anthropomorphize and admire their bravery and boldness, small birds taking on dangerous intruders, and coming to blows, too, rather than holding off at a safe distance and making a noise. At the same time, they are themselves subject to attention from piratical skuas and the less noble muggings of the black-backed gulls. And, if taken by surprise at night, they are done for: Common Terns get up and go, leaving the colony unguarded, if a night predator appears. Their defences are really daytime ones and night-fighting is not for them.

A mixed group of adult and young Common Terns in late summer, plunging for fish in coastal shallows.

2

IDENTIFICATION

THE scientific name of the Common Tern is *Sterna hirundo*. The word *'stearn'* appears in eighth-century Anglo-Saxon and 'stern' and 'stearne' are used in Old English, but the connection, if there is one, between these words and the terns is obscure. There are several Scandinavian words – *'terne'*, *'taerne'*, *'terna'* and *'tärna'* – all of which mean maidservant, but again there is no clear link with our modern tern. Nevertheless, the Gaelic word for a tern is *'stearnal'* or *'stearnan'*, and in Norfolk 'stern' and 'starn' are old names for tern.

James Fisher translated *The Seafarer*, a manuscript of a much earlier poem published in about AD1000 in the *Exeter Book*, a West Saxon manuscript. The word *'stearn'* is used and Fisher translates it as tern, in what he claimed, perhaps slightly fancifully but probably accurately enough, to be a poem about a visit to the Bass Rock in or before AD685. There is an early appearance of the word *'tearn'* in eleventh-century Anglo-Saxon, and in 1512 'Ternes' were referred to in the *Northumberland Household Book*. Turner, in *Avium praecipuarum historica*, published in 1544, wrote (apparently of the Black Tern): 'it is called in our language "sterna"'. Linnaeus later adopted *'sterna'* as the name for the genus of terns to which the Common and Arctic (but oddly enough not Black) Terns belong.

In 1678 Willughby, in *Ornithologia*, wrote: 'In Northern parts they call them Terns, whence Turner called them in Latine, Sternae, because they frequent Lakes and great Pools of water, which, in the North of England, are called Tarns'.

Several names applied to the Common Tern refer to its resemblance in shape to the Swallow.

12

This has an odd relationship with some old, faded and forgotten names in Orkney and north-east Scotland, including picktarne, tarnie and darr. Clearly, these names owe much to the calls of the bird and any connection with pools, or the tarns of northern England, is impossible to find.

The specific name – *hirundo* – is a simple reference to the Latin word for swallow. The group which includes swallows and martins is often referred to as a whole as 'hirundines', meaning swallow-like. The Common Tern is, as the name suggests, the epitome of the sea swallow, the graceful, slender-bodied bird of the air with a deeply forked tail extending into long, pointed streamers at each corner, exactly as does the Swallow's.

In their fascinating, and, sadly, little-known, book *Sea Terns or Sea Swallows* (published in 1934), George and Anne Marples give long accounts of local names for terns. Early, wrongly used names for the Common Tern include the intriguing 'cloven-footed gull', which probably in reality referred to the Black Tern. It was also called the River Tern *Sterna fluviatilis*, just one of sixteen scientific names applied to it.

The swallow reference appears in Welsh – *Gwennol y Mor* and *Morwennol gyffredin* – as well as in French (*Hirondelle de Mer*) and German (*Seeschwalbe* and *Flußseeschwalbe*). The Marples claimed that the many names including the syllable 'pick' referred to the habit of picking fish from the sea. 'Pick', all the same, is a very good representation of a common call. The list includes picktar, pickitar, picket-aa, pictarnie, pickmire and piccatarrie (all good onomatopoeic names).

Tarry, tarret, tarrack, tarrock and terrick echo the use of tarrock to describe the young Kittiwake, with its black zigzag wing pattern. 'Etymology doubtful' is all my dictionary has to say on that. Skrike, scrage, scray, skirre, spore and sparling are among those names obviously derived from calls, along with kirrmew, kirmsu, kip and clett. Rixy, meaning quarrelsome, is an excellent name, as is gull-teaser. Kingfisher is obvious; williefisher an interesting alternative. 'Spyrryd' means spirit, an evocative reference to the whiteness and grace of the bird at sea. There are plenty more names, with and without likely explanations.

Identifying terns

Turner, in 1544, referred to one bird as 'a *Larus*' – now the generic name of most gulls – and called it 'stern', apparently the Black Tern. Willughby, in 1678, referred to the terns as 'the least sort of gull, having a forked tail'. Gesner (1516–65 – one of several people accorded the title 'the father of ornithology') referred to three terns, as well as gulls, in the genus *Larus*. *Larus piscator* seems likely to have been the Common Tern. In 1662, Sir Thomas Browne wrote of 'Lari, seamews and cobs' in Norfolk, including *Larus cinereus*, apparently

Common Terns were once confused with gulls but later it was only Arctic Terns that created real problems: the black-tipped, scarlet bill, long wings relative to the tail and relatively longer legs identify this summer adult.

the Common Tern, commonly called sterne, and also writes of the 'Hirundo marina or sea-swallowe, a bird much larger than a swallow, neat, white and fork-tailed'.

The confusion with, or at least the lack of any perceived separation from, gulls continued for many years; indeed, it still does. By the time of the *General Synopsis* of Latham, in 1781, the Common Tern was well enough known for a lengthy and accurate plumage description and interesting behavioural notes to be published. He gave three names: Spurre, from Caldey Island, off the coast of South Wales (where there was an islet called Spurre Island); Scraye, from various parts of England, a name that mimicked the birds' calls; and Tern, from 'northern parts'. But even then the Arctic, Roseate and Sandwich Terns were not known or not recognized by Latham.

The careful observer, Montagu, still did not mention the Arctic Tern in his 1802 *Dictionary of British Birds*, although he was good and accurate enough to distinguish difficult species pairs like Hen and Montagu's Harriers. Linnaeus, in 1735, had made no mention of the Arctic Tern either, although it is likely that the bird he described under the name *Sterna hirundo hirundo* was actually an Arctic, not a Common Tern! Brünnich, however, had described the Arctic Tern as a separate species in 1764, despite Henry Seebohm's later assertion that the distinction was not made until 1819. Nevertheless, although the confusion between terns and gulls was largely past, the difficulties in separating the closely similar species of terns were much more deep-seated and long-lasting.

Oddly enough, although Montagu had no knowledge of the Arctic Tern, he did separate the rarer Roseate Tern. A Dr MacDougall shot one in 1813 and, realizing it was something different, he sent it to Montagu, who quickly saw its significance and named it *Sterna dougallii*. Later attempts to revive the full name of Dr MacDougall, using the English name MacDougall's Tern, failed to become established.

The identification of Common, Arctic and Roseate Terns in the field still presents a challenge worthy of the best birdwatchers. Many fail to take it on and stick too readily, too easily, to the use of 'commic tern' in their notebooks. This, a simple ducking of the issue, is shorthand for 'Common or Arctic'. It is, perhaps, a pity that the names lend themselves so well to such a combination, but even people who do try harder often struggle. Quite understandably, too, on occasion, as the trio (especially the Common/Arctic pair) are difficult and sometimes impossible to separate, but only due to circumstance: given a good enough view they should always be distinguishable.

The willingness to leave identification unsettled was, very largely, a fault of poor references in published guide books until at least the 1970s and early 1980s. Much of the hard work had been done long before, but identification guides failed to take on board the advances that had been made in separating these tricky birds. It is strange that the competition for shelf (and pocket) space in a period of rapidly expanding interest in popular bird identification did not result in any book putting one over on the others by trying to sort out the more challenging identification crises, the terns in particular.

The underwing pattern of the Common Tern is the same at all ages: the opaque outer primary feathers and broad dusky trailing edge separate it from the Arctic Tern overhead.

For many years, the separation of Common from Arctic rested on quite correct but difficult features such as leg length and bill colour. A flying tern at long range, or against the light, or in grey rain or mist, rarely gives a chance to judge the length of its leg or the precise colour and pattern of its bill. If it perched, perhaps the relative lengths of tail and closed wingtips would help. There were also odd hints that some calls might be useful, too.

As for young ones, and adults in winter plumage, nothing of any help was offered by the popular guides, although there were some clues in the detailed works such as *The Handbook of British Birds* by Witherby and his remarkable team of experts, who pushed back the frontiers of both ornithological publishing and field expertise.

John Walpole-Bond, in his essay on the Common Tern in his three-volume review of the birds of Sussex, simply reminded the reader that these terns were 'damnably difficult' to identify in the field. T.A. Coward, in his excellent *The Birds of the British Isles and their Eggs*, published in 1920, mentioned the differences in bill colour but stressed that the pair was tricky, to say the least, in the field, although the two species were generally easily separated in the hand. The safest feature, he said, was the pattern of grey and white on the outer primary feather.

It was the late Richard Richardson, whose initials R.A.R. still grace many published drawings of immense skill and economy of line, who began to see better ways of telling a Common Tern from an Arctic when they were actually alive and free and flying around one's head. Richard, generally in his brown leather jacket and black beret or woolly hat, lived and birdwatched at Cley in Norfolk from 1940, driving along the coast road on his big motorbike, using his small binoculars to great effect. His fantastic eyesight and eye for a bird meant that he rarely needed a telescope, although I well remember the time I let him briefly borrow mine – quite something for a young birdwatcher in awe of his abilities. The Norfolk coast, the shingle beach of Blakeney Point and the lagoons of Arnold's Marsh, were perfect for a tern-watcher, and R.A.R. made the most of his opportunities.

The *Collins Pocket Guide to British Birds* by R.S.R. Fitter (who effectively discovered Richard Richardson as an artist) and R.A. Richardson, when first published in 1952, gave the usual summary of field marks. Only later editions included a fine and more complete discussion of identification features, mentioning differences in underwing pattern and translucency noted by Richardson. His paintings in the guide, prepared before 1952, do nothing to show them.

In fact Richard Richardson published his ideas in 1953, in an illustrated note in *British Birds* ('*BB*'), always the place to make public such important findings. He credited Mr Gordon Rayner for first drawing to his attention a character that was 'widely used by observers in Scandinavia and the Low Countries' but which had been overlooked by British writers. He showed that, not only did the black tips to the outer primaries make a different pattern on the Common Tern compared with the Arctic, but the whole of the primary feathers showed a different character when viewed against the light. On the Arctic Tern, these feathers look pale and translucent; on the Common, only the innermost four primaries have this pale appearance, making a distinctive light patch behind the bend of the wing.

With sun shining through, the inner primaries (and the inner webs of the outer ones if they are sufficiently spread) of a Common Tern look translucent.

The editorial comment accompanying the note said that 'even in this country, this difference has long been used by some', but also queried whether it was really 100 per cent reliable, as Richardson had claimed (although he, after all, had looked at hundreds of terns and found that it always worked).

A Field Guide to the Birds of Britain and Europe by Peterson, Mountfort and Hollom, another Collins publication of 1954 (and a true break-through), did not at first include the Richardson identification points. Birdwatchers without *BB* had to wait for later editions of this and the *Pocket Guide* to find out about the new ideas on tern identification. Later editions of the *Field Guide* managed a good summary of identification points for adult terns, but again missed the opportunity properly to illustrate what was being described with reference to the underwings. In 1972, Heinzel, Fitter and Parslow published *The Birds of Britain and Europe with North Africa and the Middle East*, and at least the paintings made a stab at showing the proper pattern, although with little accuracy.

In America, the Peterson guide, *A Field Guide to the Birds*, did not include the wing patterns until the fully revised version (really a new book) appeared in 1980. Roger Tory Peterson invented the field guide, to all intents and purposes, but his early books (like the one he illustrated on Britain and Europe) had illustrations on plates scattered through the text pages and were supposedly difficult to use. In putting text opposite plate in his new American guide, he got the patterns right on the illustration but simply had too little space to write more than a line about them. Following the trend and demands of birdwatchers for 'text opposite picture' was all well and good, but compromised the value of the book by reducing the available space.

Upperwing as well as underwing pattern on adult Common Terns became accepted as important features only in the 1970s.

Meanwhile, the importance of the pattern of the upperwings had been overlooked in the attempts to get the underwing right. In the late 1960s, I began to see and sketch differences and found them to be consistent, and they also checked out well enough on published photographs. I wrote a note to the monthly journal *British Birds*, thinking that I was on to something new, only to be told by the then editor, Pat Bonham, that he and others had been using these marks for years. It was a response curiously like the editor's comment appended to Richard Richardson's 1953 note.

The late Peter Grant, always keenly interested in terns (and already responsible for working out the identification problems and their solutions for juveniles), was nevertheless very interested ('and if that's so', he said, 'why didn't they tell anyone?'). Between us we drafted a paper for *BB*, which was published early in 1974. Meanwhile, Pat Bonham had found references to the same pattern by a Belgian, J.-P. Vande Weghe, in *Aves* of 1966. So much for being first with anything.

Overlooked for years, Vande Weghe's characters, revived by Hume and Grant, provided a new way for observers to pick out Common from Arctic Terns and vice versa, which sometimes worked on birds flying a mile away! Quite literally, the infinitely difficult Common and Arctic Terns, so often pushed aside as 'commics', suddenly became quite easy at very long range – sometimes.

The field guides were still slow to catch on. Lars Jonsson, whose superb eye and wonderful artistic ability made his set of small field guides to European birds a collector's item, produced fine illustrations in *Birds of Sea and Coast* in 1977 (English translation, 1978). Otherwise, few did justice to the upperwing differences.

Strangely enough, it was practically all there in the Marples' book, all the time. Not only are there excellent photographs of live birds, but the book has some extremely useful black-and-white photographs of specimens, showing the upperside and underside of spread wings, spread tails and outer primary feathers (which clearly illustrate the differences relied upon by Coward). The major drawback is that a Common Tern specimen is shown photographed only from above, an Arctic only from below. Had that not been so, someone might have sorted out the Common from the 'commic' long ago. The Marples themselves simply settled for the statement that: 'In the air the Common Tern cannot, with certainty, be distinguished from the Arctic.'

The upperside of an adult Arctic Tern's wing has a fresh, clean look about it, with a tendency to get paler towards the tip.

The upperwing of an adult Common Tern shows a contrast between the outermost five primary feathers and the rest, unlike any Arctic.

At the same time, the Roseate Tern caused confusion. It was too often described – perhaps as a result of its display flight, but more likely simply through repetition of mistakes generated by ignorance of the living bird – as exceptionally elegant and graceful. In fact, despite its long tail-streamers, the Roseate Tern has relatively short wings, and bats along at speed almost like a Little Tern. Its direct flight is less elegant, easy and graceful than either the Common or the Arctic Tern's, of which more later.

Of the juveniles, nothing much was ever said. The great Witherby *Handbook* had adequate descriptions but little help in the way of field marks. Once the underwing translucency and pattern of dark tips to the outer primaries were sorted out by Richard Richardson, they became easier (because this was just as good for juveniles as for adults). But identification still rested all too often on the adults that accompanied them. Odd illustrations – such as the one in *The Handbook* which gives the young Roseate Tern orange-yellow legs – failed to throw much light on them and, worse, added to the confusion.

Then along came Bob Scott, at the time warden at Dungeness in Kent, and Peter Grant, making a name for himself as a gull and tern specialist of no mean ability. Bob, big and booming, bearded and jocular, went on to greater things in the Royal Society for the Protection of Birds, while maintaining his reputation as a fine field observer. Peter became one of the leading lights of bird identification, Chairman of the Rarities Committee, probing and critically constructive in his approach, ever ready to tackle the most difficult of subjects (such as rare stints) until his sad, early death. Between them they wrote, and Peter illustrated, a breakthrough paper on the field identification of young Common, Arctic and Roseate Terns, published in 1969 in *British Birds*.

Bob tells me that he and Peter first took an interest in terns over 'the patch', an area of warm water welling up from the outflow from the Dungeness power station. It was a one-year-old tern, in a strange plumage that had been seen before and termed '*portlandica*', that caught their eye first. They produced a *BB* note on that, too. But gradually they noticed that some young terns looked different from others and they tried to work them out. Roseate Terns, in spring, 'like budgerigars with such long tails, but pink', struck Bob Scott as quite easy, but what of the juveniles in autumn? 'We decided to visit Anglesey to see what could be found out on an island where all three bred, then took back the knowledge we had gained to Dungeness and applied it to local and migrant terns there, to see if it still worked.' It did, of course.

I remember this as a paper that influenced me greatly at the time. I spent many hours at reservoirs in south Staffordshire and was beginning a period of intense birdwatching in South Wales, living beside Swansea Bay. I tested the techniques described by Grant and Scott for myself and, predictably, that they worked. I was finding young Common and Arctic Terns surprisingly easy – much easier than adults – while those birdwatchers who did not read *BB* still struggled, and usually gave up none the wiser. Since then, young terns have been a piece of cake – well, almost. Later, to co-author a paper with Peter (in the late 1960s still just a name to me) was a real honour.

Other aspects of terns began to be mentioned and these helped in identifying them. Peter Grant pointed out the importance of the differing moult patterns between Common and Arctic Terns, especially with regard to the primary feathers. This explained why I had been seeing odd Arctic Terns in late October in Staffordshire with still-complete black caps, while some Commons had white foreheads by early autumn. It also helped because an adult Common/Arctic Tern, in August or September, with its inner primaries in moult, had to be a Common. Suddenly, ragged-winged terns, some with straggly tails and even white foreheads in late summer and autumn, became obvious Commons, because Arctics did not begin to moult their primaries until they were in their winter quarters, much later in the year. Simple!

Even now most people do not recognize this difference or use it as they should. Of course, there were caveats added to the original papers and notes. Juvenile Arctic Terns with bills almost the colour of those of juvenile Common Terns were noted and described, and so on, but there has not yet been any significant contradiction of these fundamental identification papers relating to the pair of birds that, with Willow and Marsh Tits and Willow Warbler and Chiffchaff, always formed one of the most difficult species pairs in British and European birdwatching.

Description and moult

The Common Tern is a slim, lightweight seabird. From bill tip to tail tip it is about 33–35 cm (13–14 in), compared with a Black-headed Gull's 38 cm (15 in). It weighs 100–140 g, compared with the gull's 250–350 g. In length there is little in it, but the gull is two or three times as heavy, giving a much clearer idea of the real bulk of the bird in the field. An Arctic Tern measures 35 cm, because of its longer tail-streamers, but weighs only 80–110 g.

An adult Common Tern has a jet-black cap, complete in breeding plumage, from the top of the bill to the back of the neck and down to the lower eyelid. The line of the gape is separated from the cap by white, broader than the white line on the Arctic Tern. A Roseate Tern has a more domed head, with the cap angled down more onto the hindneck, often exaggerated by a more upright stance. Even in flight, the Roseate Tern sometimes has an appreciably broader, more rounded look to the black head.

The upperside of a Common Tern is soft, pale grey. A Roseate is paler above, an Arctic Tern much the same as a Common. The rump of an adult Common Tern is white, faintly suffused with grey in winter; the cheeks are white, blending into the greyer underside of the body. On an Arctic, the grey is a touch darker, the white cheeks a fraction more contrasting (sometimes this 'white streak' effect can be quite obvious, but a lot depends on the light). The underside of a Common Tern is a soft pale grey, sometimes with a pinkish or lilac tinge; on an Arctic Tern the underside looks rather smokier, whereas the underside of a Roseate Tern is essentially nearly white, with more or less of a pink tinge.

The upperwing on a Common Tern shows narrow white leading and trailing edges. Sometimes the inner webs of the secondary feathers (of which only the tips show) wear darker, giving a darker subterminal bar, which varies according to the angle of view. 'Against the grain' the grey feathers look darker than from the opposite direction, like the pile on velvet curtains.

The four or five inner primary feathers are pale grey with white tips and just the merest hint of a dark shaft. The rest are curiously different. As with all gulls and terns, there are ten large primary feathers visible on the open wing (the tiny outermost we can forget about). The outer five or six on a Common Tern have a pale grey bloom, like the bloom on a grape or a fresh sloe, which wears away to reveal blackish barbs beneath. The shafts are thick, stiff and white; the outer webs are blackish. The outer two feathers are less black on the inner webs than the next few. As the feathers get older, so the wear and tear of ordinary life rubs away the pale bloom. Opening and closing the wings, as well as active flight, rubs the feathers together and the overlapping parts become progressively blacker.

The Common Tern moults its primaries, starting with the innermost one, in early autumn, even as early as late July (or, much more rarely, at the end of May or in June). The first, then another two or three, are shed and replaced before the bird migrates south for the winter. At the same time some secondaries and coverts are shed, producing a ragged line of white across the upperwing, an untidy impression and one of which an Arctic would be thoroughly ashamed. The tail is partially moulted before autumn migration. The outer primary feathers remain unchanged, as moult is suspended. Later in the year the moult resumes, and the outer feathers are replaced. For a time, in winter, the whole outer primary area looks pale and silvery.

In the following spring, before the migration back north, the inner feathers are shed and replaced again. That means that a Common Tern reaching Europe or North America in spring has brand new inner primaries, of pristine pearly grey, and older outer ones, which can look contrastingly dark. The oldest feather is the one in the middle, contrasting most strongly with the new, pale ones. By the autumn, the outer primary feathers are worn and much blacker, while the inner ones remain pale until they are again replaced.

Roseate Terns in spring have a distinctive ghostly pallor, as well as a characteristically black bill, but in late summer the bill is partly red.

On an Arctic Tern, the primaries are all of similar colour, if anything becoming paler towards the wingtip, adding to its physical lightness of touch. Also, the moult is simpler: all the feathers are replaced late in the year, after the migration. In the spring they are all are of similar age, and all of them remain unchanged until after the bird leaves its northern haunts in the autumn. Consequently, there is no contrast between inner and outer primaries on the Arctic Tern and they always look paler overall.

On a perched bird, the pale inner primaries are usually extremely obvious on a Common Tern – a few pale feather tips protruding beyond the closed secondaries – whereas there is no such mark to be detected on an Arctic.

On the underwing, there is a broad, dark trailing edge cut off square on the outer five or six primaries. On an Arctic Tern, the outer seven feathers have thinner, dark grey tips, creating a narrow trailing edge which tapers neatly into a long, thin line.

Also, as Richardson noticed, all the primaries (and secondaries) on an Arctic Tern look semi-transparent against a bright sky. On a Common Tern, only the inner four look like this, making a paler patch against the opaque outer secondaries and outer primaries. This is often obvious on a bird overhead, but also quite visible on a bird flying low against the light. Beware the bird overhead with the underwing lit strongly by the sun from one side: the primaries look full, bright white and will be translucent only if some light is coming through from behind.

In the hand, on a bird trapped for ringing or picked up dead, the differences in primary pattern regarded as so sure by T.A. Coward can be seen. On a Common Tern, the outer web is thin and black, the shaft white, and the inner web white with a dark tip. A long wedge of grey or black extends from the tip along the shaft; this is less broad than the white band, around a third of the width of the whole web. On an Arctic, the dark tips are narrower and the dark band along the shaft very narrow, less than a quarter the width of the whole inner web. At 10 mm from the tip, the grey is 3–5 mm wide on a Common Tern, and 1·5–2·5 mm wide on an Arctic.

The outermost primary feather (except for a tiny one, usually hidden) is also broader on a Common Tern than on an Arctic, and the five outer primaries of an Arctic are tapered more finely to narrower points than those of the Common Tern.

The outer tail feathers are long and flexible at the tips, especially on an Arctic Tern. On a Common Tern the whole outer web of the outer feather is 'aluminium grey' deepening to practically black; on an Arctic, it is deep grey but paler along a line close to the shaft.

In spring, an adult Common Tern has a bright vermilion, or orange-red, bill with a black or dark brownish tip. The extreme tip, just the tiniest speck, is often an almost colourless, or fingernail-coloured, semi-transparent spot that sometimes catches the light or shines against the sun. Its legs are vivid red. An Arctic Tern has deep red legs, and a bill of blood-red or deep scarlet, without the black at the tip. In summer some Commons have little black, but the difference holds good in 99 cases out of a hundred. In any case, the orange-red or vermilion is generally distinctly different from the deep red of the Arctic's beak. The Roseate Tern has a blacker looking bill, with dark red at the base in spring, but by late summer often half, even two-thirds, becomes rich orange-red, leaving a large black tip reminiscent of the Common Tern. The bill of a Common Tern is rather stout and long; that of the Arctic is shorter, deeper-based, but sharp-tipped.

In winter, both Common and Arctic Terns have white foreheads, blackish bills (usually with a little red at the base on the Common) and duller legs. The Common also has a blackish band along the front edge of the inner wing (less obvious on an Arctic). The white forehead marks that begin to show on a Common Tern in autumn are often due to wear and tear, allowing the white feather bases to show through, as relatively few begin their head and body moult before migrating south. The body of a Common Tern in winter is strikingly white, without the soft greys of summer plumage on the underparts.

Immature plumages

Juveniles are interesting and, as I have already mentioned, sometimes easier than their parents to tell apart. Commons share their parents' slightly heavier, broader appearance compared with Arctics, but all young terns begin their flying career on shorter, more rounded wings than adults, and are consequently quicker, and more flappy, in their flight. Juvenile Commons look grey, white and black, but with more or less of a gingery-brown tinge on top. Young Arctics, although marked quite heavily with scaly crescents above, tend to look a purer grey and white at a distance.

Young Common Terns have fleshy-pink (even orange-yellow) bills with a dark tip, which gradually darken to black-brown with less pale red at the base (even virtually all black on a few by September). They have dull pinkish-red or yellow-orange legs. Arctics have effectively black bills, with a little fleshy-red at the base at first, and red or dark brown legs. The bill colour is usually a good feature to look for.

Both have white foreheads, and black on the crown, nape and down the sides of the head in a neat cap, like a fur hat with turned-down ear flaps. The Common has a browner or gingery tinge over the forehead, making it less clean than the Arctic, although this quickly wears off. The rump of a young Common Tern shows pale grey down the centre, although many feathers are more or less tipped with white. On an Arctic it is pure white.

The underwings are like those of the adults. Above, the Common Tern has the leading edge of the inner wing almost blackish. The rest of the wing-coverts are paler, the greater coverts (along the midwing or just behind) almost milky grey. Feathers of the back, scapulars and wing-coverts have a pattern of grey base and a buff-brown band before a white tip. The scapulars and tertials, in particular, may have an almost blackish or sepia brown crescentic band or irregular mottles. The secondaries are darker grey with white tips, forming a grey band across the hindwing.

On an Arctic Tern, the upperwing is essentially dark at the front, grey in the middle and white at the back, as the inner primaries and secondaries are the palest grey with broad white tips. There is no grey band across the hindwing at all, instead a long triangle of white – one of the best features to check on a young tern. Young Arctics, like adults, are also lighter, smaller, more delicate than young Commons, if anything the smallest and daintiest of all.

A soft greyness is distinctive on a summer adult Arctic Tern, as is the short, spiky, all-red bill and really tiny legs.

Roseate Terns at this age are tricky, but are more coarsely marked on top, have dark foreheads with little or no real white, and black legs. Like the adults, their primaries seen from underneath are a real give-away: there may be a dusky line towards the tip, but the tips of the feathers are see-through white, and there is no black trailing edge.

Until the Grant and Scott paper all this was poorly known, and even later few people seemed to comprehend it. I saw records of young 'Roseates' with orange legs accepted and published by county record committees, while my own of a pair of Roseates, one a young bird scaled all over on top with blackish grey, with a dark forehead, black bill and black legs (and the other an adult washed with pink!), was rejected out of hand.

What of the mysterious *'portlandica'*? This strange apparition was first noticed as a peculiarly contrasty-looking tern with black bill, white forehead and dark forewing (carpal) bars, but also blackish outer primaries and outer tail feathers, in spring and summer. It became clear, eventually, that this is how Common (and Arctic) Terns look when they are one year old, that is in first-summer plumage. We see few in Europe or North America because birds of this age generally stay in their winter quarters all year through. They are rare in the north and cause a few headaches when they do appear. Apart from the blackish areas, white forehead and black bill, there are other marks that vary individually, principally the number of juvenile feathers with brown subterminal bars that may be retained.

The moult of these immature terns is actually complicated and difficult to be entirely sure about. By the mid-winter of the tern's first year of life, the outer wing feathers are worn and six or eight months old. From about January to July, the flight feathers are slowly replaced, so the outer ones look almost black between February and June while the inner ones look neat and pale.

Immatures still not in breeding condition the following year – the third calendar year of their life (second-summer birds, two years old) – are variable. Some look much like the first-summers, but without the blacker outer primaries, and sometimes with more red on the bill; others are more advanced with adult-like plumage except for whiter underparts and some white on the forehead. A few look just like adults except that they are paler, almost white, below. A further year on, some are still showing white on the forehead and some dark marks on the wing-coverts, but even a few adults show such marks, so without further evidence, such as a ring, it is not possible to age birds by this stage.

Enough of the detail. What really matters is how the birds look, alive and well and flying free, or, as the text books have it, in the field. Common Terns always look beautifully elegant and light, airy and full of the bright light and whispering breeze that they ride upon for most of their life. They are a delight. Yet, by comparison, they are heavy and solid after you have watched an Arctic Tern in full flow.

Arctics are at their best around some northern island or headland, perhaps around a pile of red sandstone or pink granite rocks jutting from the deep water of a Scottish sea loch. They flit and swoop and twist around, bright and white-winged, delicate and supremely free in their actions in the air.

Arctic Terns have long wings tweaked to a narrow tip, the outermost part a long, fine point with a hint of a backward curve. Common Terns' wings are more regularly triangular, a touch broader, a trifle heavier-looking overall. More than that, a Common Tern has a bigger, longer head on a longer neck (although it is purely relative – the neck is still short and stubby). Mr Vande Weghe noticed this difference in proportion and wrote it up very well. The area of the head, neck and bill of a Common Tern sticks forward quite a way, and the tail balances it behind the wings. On an Arctic Tern, the bill is a fraction shorter, the head rounder, the neck short, thick, almost not there at all, and the tail-streamers longer when fresh and undamaged. Consequently, the Common

'Portlandica', or first-summer Common Terns retain old, blackish outer primaries and secondaries and have a white forehead all summer.

A practised eye can tell Common from Arctic Terns in silhouette, the neckless, dumpy Arctics (A) with fine-tipped wings appreciably different from the longer-headed, longer-winged Commons (C).

Tern has more in front and less behind than an Arctic, which is all wings and tail with the body blending directly into the short head. It makes up for this slightly hunched look with its lightness of flight and the translucency of its flight feathers.

A Common Tern in flight seems stable and direct, although it has not quite got the purposeful, powerful progress of the larger Sandwich Tern. An Arctic is more bouncy and at the mercy of the wind, although it is an even greater traveller of the oceans. The Common Tern has a fast, powerful downstroke but a faintly lumbering look about it. The Arctic is fluttery, butterfly-like, with a quick, snapped upstroke and a slower downbeat: it is easier to see the downstroke than the upbeat. The shorter-winged Roseate has a stiffer action, with upstrokes and downstrokes of equal speed and emphasis.

Common and Arctic Terns behave slightly differently. A fishing tern will often hover, looking down into the water to spot a fish. Once the fish has been spotted, the tern dives down, hits the water with a splash and flies up again, perhaps with a gleaming silvery fish in its bill. The manner of diving, however, varies.

We turn again to *British Birds* for a good description of this. In 1987 Dr Ian Kirkham, of Canada, and Dr I.C.T. Nisbet, a British expert long resident in the USA, wrote a fascinating paper. Typically, they record, the Common Tern flies along, looking down, then swoops gently upwards, turns back slightly and plunges in. The Arctic, however, is more hesitant and hovers, moves, hovers, then dips down, pauses part-way through the dive, hovers momentarily again to check all is well, then plunges. The Roseate Tern has a more confident method, flying along, seeing a fish and simply turning downhill to 'fly into the water'.

Once familiar with one or the other, it is usually not so much of a problem to distinguish Common and Arctic at a distance using their distinctive character in the air, but it is easy to overstate this. It is fine when there is a flock of Arctics around some Orkney isle or Scottish headland, but a single bird or small group over a reservoir inland may be much less easy. Despite all the refinements of jizz and character, wing translucency and upperwing pattern, some are still plain hard to tell.

Geographical variation

The Common Terns of North America and Europe are effectively identical, except that the wing length (as measured from the bend of the closed wing to the tip) is somewhat shorter, on average, in North America. The difference is about 6·5 mm. These are nevertheless treated as being of the same race, *hirundo*.

There is a different race, *longipennis*, in eastern Siberia. This is a slightly darker bird, with a black bill in summer and very dark legs and feet. It is a fraction larger in terms of wing length, but has a shorter bill than more western birds, but there is no firm dividing line and in the area of overlap it is impossible to put many birds into one race or the other. Some *longipennis* features may be found in birds breeding as far west as the Ob basin. These birds generally have more black on the bill tip than *hirundo*, or wholly black bills and other features tending more towards the *longipennis* characteristics. The birds in this area used to be termed *minussensis*, but, as they are like one or other of the other races, or intermediate, it is not really practical to treat them as a race apart, although the new checklist, *A Complete Checklist of the Birds of the World – second edition* by Richard Howard and Alick Moore, published in 1991, does so and may be right.

Another good race, however, is *tibetana*, which covers the Common Terns from the central Asian mountains. Here they look dark, like *longipennis*, long-winged and short-billed, but with both legs and bill as red as any well-bred *hirundo*. In winter, when all of these races have blacker bills, they are not really worth trying to tell apart.

3

THE TERN IN
ITS ENVIRONMENT

MUCH of the story of the Common Tern is intertwined with its habitat requirements. Habitat determines nesting and feeding possibilities, so, before looking at other details of the tern's life, a brief review of its preferred environment is essential.

To quote *The Birds of the Western Palearctic*, the Common Tern 'breeds over wider spectrum of habitats than other *Sterna*: from Arctic fringe through boreal, temperate, steppe, Mediterranean and semi-desert zones to tropics, both along coasts and on inland fresh waters, mainly in lowland but up to 300 m or more in Scotland, to 2000 m in Armenia and 4400–4800 m in Asia.'

It is a remarkable variety for a bird that basically needs clear water with fish in it and a piece of bare ground to nest on. Of course, it is these essentially simple basic requirements that allow the Common Tern to find a niche, somewhere or other, in all the varied kinds of places described in *The Birds of the Western Palearctic*. In most parts of the world there will be a shoreline, the junction between the water and land that make up the tern's world.

It does, however, have particular preferences, and not just any old shoreline will do. It avoids icy waters (whereas Arctic Terns often sit about on ice floes), and decidedly dislikes places that are regularly subject to strong winds or heavy rain. Neither tall vegetation nor sheer cliffs or rough, broken, rocky coasts suit it well. It prefers low, rather flat, softer ground with an all-round view.

What it does like may be provided by slabs of flat rocks by the sea, open shingle or sandy beaches and firm, established sand dunes. Islands are often best, because they are less disturbed, but mainland beaches and peninsular dunes are fine, if they are not full of holiday-makers, foxes or hedgehogs.

In Shetland, Common Terns nest mainly on shingle beaches or flat rocks along the shore. In Orkney, the tern colonies are mixed, on shingle, rough pasture just inland, and on rising heathery ground. The Shetlands and Orkneys are fantastic places for Arctic Terns. They nest mostly on shingle or sand, but also on storm beaches – the ones with swathes of big stones and pebbles around the head of a bay – and on low rocks in Shetland. The highest densities of breeding terns of both species in Orkney and Shetland are found on shingle beaches; the biggest colonies,

In western Scotland Common Terns nest on rocky coastal islets.

however, are on the inland heath and grassland. These are frequently mixed, with Common Terns generally in smaller numbers. The Common Terns, perhaps helped by their longer legs, tend to go for the longer vegetation in a mixed colony, although they do not go to such extremes as Roseate Terns, which frequently nest under overhanging herbs or even deep in jungles of tree mallow.

The colonies in the northern isles of Britain are in some of the most wonderful bird habitats of Europe. Offshore will be crooning Eiders, Red-breasted Mergansers taking a break from their nests hidden in the shoreline grass, and Red-throated Divers, which have flown down from their nesting lochans to feed in the clear sea. Black Guillemots, little dots that frequently disappear underwater and pop up again like corks, breed in the fallen boulders and broken rocks of the headlands and feed in the sheltered bays. There are marauding Great Black-backed Gulls and both Arctic and Great Skuas. The skuas bathe in freshwater lakes inland, and Arctics display in exciting, high-speed rollercoaster dives and swoops with the most wonderful nasal, wailing calls. Around the rocky shores are Ringed Plovers, Rock Pipits and dark, heavily barred Wrens of the local island race. Perhaps a rare Red-necked Phalarope appears for a quick dip; or a couple of lingering Whooper Swans, or Long-tailed Ducks, or sparkling chequerboard-patterned Great Northern Divers are also in the bay. The terns have many notable neighbours, but hold their own against them in terms of visual appeal and sheer elegance of form.

In the Outer Hebrides many a skerry has a small ternery, often Arctics but with a scattering of Commons. Sandy beaches between little, low headlands of dark rock, or banks of shingle and broken shell, provide lovely and secure places for them to lay eggs. Their neighbours are the bumbling Eiders, ear-splitting Oystercatchers and squealing Common Gulls. Now and then a Greylag Goose peers over the edge of the dunes from the machair where it has its downy goslings. Out to sea, sometimes the sinuous form of an otter excites the tern-watcher, although so far as the terns are concerned the otter can just as well take a dive and never come up again. It is occasionally a rapacious predator of terns, adults and chicks alike. The glorious Hebrides in a summer calm are all blue and green and white sand, the sea silky smooth or agleam and glittering where catspaws snatch at the surface and raise myriad ripples which catch the last of the evening sun. It is still light at midnight, when the piping of the Oystercatchers and the repetitive rasp of the Corncrake sharpen our appreciation of the otherwise calm and silent surroundings.

Farther south, the shingle beaches are as likely to be occupied by Little Terns, which have a much narrower habitat selection than the Commons. There are a few shell banks, too, which attract Little and Common Terns. These are really exposed, absolutely bare and few birds can cope with them for long. Oystercatchers and Ringed Plovers are the likely species to nest close to the terns here.

Bare ground or short vegetation is preferred for nesting, but where grass and shrubs have grown up in a previously occupied bare site, such as the upper edge of a firm, mud beach, or even an island in a freshwater lake, the terns may persist through a determination to hang on to a good thing long after it has begun to deteriorate towards the untenable. Indeed, their own droppings over many years may create the vegetation problem in the first place by fertilizing the sward.

Below the big cliffs which house the colonies of Guillemots, Razorbills and Kittiwakes, terns are not generally found nesting unless there are some low, rocky islets offshore. Then there may be Common, Arctic, even Roseate Terns together with Herring, Common and Lesser Black-backed Gulls, a little away from the noise and bustle of the auk cities. It is, especially in the north, more usual to see Arctic Terns than Common Terns in such spots.

On a saltmarsh, Common Terns often nest close to Black-headed Gulls. It is a debatable point which look the best in such situations, the terns with their coal-black caps or the gulls with plum-coloured beaks and chocolate brown hoods. They avoid the lowest part of the marsh (although some do nest below the highest spring-tide mark) and also the upper, drier edge, where disturbance is likely to be greater. They feed away from the marsh, while most other nesters on a saltmarsh feed within it. The marsh vegetation may be dominated by a number of plants, but is generally low, often very short, with some exposed ridges of shells, sand or shingle here and there and often deep, steep-sided creeks. The marsh in spring and summer may be coloured purple and blue by sea lavender, or bathed in pink by flowering thrift, cut across by crescents of glistening blue standing water. In these underrated, colourful and expansive surroundings, the Common Terns and Black-headed Gulls will have Oystercatchers, Redshanks and now and then a Shelduck or two, or a few pairs of Skylarks and Meadow Pipits, as neighbours.

Inland nesting is frequent and, of course, over much of eastern Europe and Asia is the only option. A variety of marshy sites, lakes with heaps of dead vegetation more or less floating against the shore, grassy islands and shingle banks in larger rivers offer likely nesting sites for small colonies.

In Britain, the spread of Common Terns breeding inland has largely been related to the increase in flooded gravel diggings, which often provide just the right kind of islands with stony or sandy ground rather than the reedy or overgrown banks of most natural lakes. The Common Tern is one of three species – along with Little Ringed Plover and Great Crested Grebe – for which flooded gravel workings have been cited as of real importance in lowland England. Nevertheless, Common Terns find them a touch too insecure to persist for long in most places. Growth of vegetation, the increase in disturbance (from fishermen, sailors, water-skiers and the like) and sometimes perhaps the competition from other species tend to move them on.

One island in a large pit that I know well used to have several hundred pairs of Black-headed Gulls and ten to twenty pairs of terns breeding annually. Now it is empty, except for large feeding flocks (and odd breeding pairs) of feral Greylag Geese. I do not know if it is the geese that have driven off the gulls and terns or not. There always

Natural marshes and man-made coastal lagoons provide island nest sites for Common Terns.

were a few geese. The local farmer's predilection for low-level flying of his microlight aircraft along the pit is another reason put forward for the desertion. Another colony nearby went under because of persistent, deliberate disturbance, probably to rid the place of birds that might have interfered with planning permission for development. The site is now a marina.

Although we think of them as birds of wide-open spaces, with a good all-round view and plenty of free airspace, the inland Common Terns are not always averse to flying between the tree-tops beside a flooded pit. The Cambridgeshire ones I watch regularly zoom about close to the tops of waterside willows and poplars and often follow the course of the Great Ouse where it is overhung by ancient trees, bowed over by the years and the damp. Occasionally they perch on the dead branches of a couple of trees killed off by the rising waters of a flooded gravel pit.

Good news for inland terns is that they will take readily to artificial rafts anchored offshore in flooded pits or natural lakes. A large, substantial wooden raft built up with low sheltering walls around a gravel-covered top makes an ideal, generally disturbance-free site for a small tern colony. The walls seem necessary to stop unwary chicks from falling overboard and drowning. A number of strange artificial sites of this sort have been used – indeed, Common Terns have been known to nest on factory roofs, too.

In eastern England, where I know inland terns best, Common Terns breed beside the flooded gravel pits but often forage along rivers. Birds that follow the Great Ouse are often to be seen over the town centre of Bedford, or crossing the A1 anywhere between Biggleswade and Huntingdon. It is a slightly incongruous, but welcome, sight, a Common Tern overhead as one is carrying bags of shopping back to the car park. They tend to keep up at roof-top height rather than down near water-level with the gulls, as if they are determined to pass through the town to quieter reaches as soon as they can. Somehow the occasional urban appearance reflects the adaptability, success and wide distribution which are such characteristic attributes of the species.

Outside the breeding season, the quality of the land becomes less of a problem for the terns. It is more the water and what is in it that interests them. All they need apart from fish is a place to perch now and then, and a safe place to spend the night. That may be best provided, not by a shingle beach or offshore rock, but by a water-skiers' raft, a trout-release cage, a yacht-club buoy, a pier or even a moored boat. The need for a safe breeding site has gone – just something free from predators and general disturbance will do.

Terns are often seen inland, even where they do not breed, on migration, but larger lakes, reservoirs and pits are still the most likely

In some breeding areas and more generally outside the breeding season Common Terns make extensive use of man-made objects as perches.

In much of eastern and central England Common Terns now nest beside flooded gravel pits.

---

places. At some, gatherings of fifty or even one hundred Common Terns in late summer and autumn are possible, but at most places they are of irregular appearance, a few at a time, usually staying an hour or two before moving on. Where available, they will prefer to perch on buoys and rafts. I have rarely seen them gather on the shore of a reservoir or lake, except where there are, for whatever reason, discrete stretches of sand or shingle. They do not tend to stand about anywhere along a shore, as do many migrant waders.

Along the coast they are widespread, especially in autumn when things are more relaxed and the pace of life is much more slack than it is in the urgency of spring. Estuaries, shingle banks, sand bars, shallow coastal lagoons, all have visitations from flocks of terns. They follow the tide in and out, every so often diving in with a smack to catch some small, luckless fish. If a shoal of fish rises to the surface, a bickering, over-excited flock of terns will gather for a time, striking while the fish are exposed. Some warm-water outfalls from industrial sites or power stations attract terns, and they may also hover around the fringe of the flocks of bigger gulls at a discharging sewage pipe. They are essential parts of the late summer and early autumn scene on many a stretch of coast. Then, one day, they are gone; the tern population has moved on south.

In the winter, the Common Terns are along the west coast of Africa. They gather at fishing quays and piers, perching in mixed groups with the rare Roseate Terns, small Black Terns and stocky Sandwich Terns. Standing above them all are some substantially bigger, orange-billed Royal Terns. Overhead may pass a Scottish or Scandinavian Osprey and each dawn and dusk legions of egrets fly from and to their night-time roosts.

In sheltered lagoons behind sandy beaches the terns regularly rest in dense flocks, while a collection of Kentish and Kittlitz's Plovers, Wood Sandpipers, Ruffs, stilts and godwits feed around them. They hear the strange, descending whistles of Grey Hornbills, the duets of Gonoleks and the sad, poo-poo-pooing diminuendos of Spotted Wood Doves. With date palms and baobabs as a backdrop, the scene can hardly be more unlike the cold, harsh shores of northern Europe, but here the terns will stay during the few months of the northern winter and young ones will remain for the first year or two of their lives.

4

DISTRIBUTION
AND POPULATIONS

LOOKING down on a map with the breeding distribution of the Common Tern marked on it (*see page 6*), you would see a broad band which almost encircled the North Pole, but with curious differences between the Old World and the New.

Some bird species have a circumpolar range that is much more tightly contained within a ring around the Arctic: the Arctic Tern is much more like that, although it does have outlying groups farther south. The Snowy Owl is a better example of a truly circumpolar species.

Few birds match the grace of terns in flight.

While the Arctic Tern's distribution completes the ring, however, the Common Tern's is broken in western North America and, in Europe and Asia, it is also more drawn down into increasingly broken areas of distribution extending farther south.

In the New World, Common Terns breed over much of northern Canada and the extreme northern fringe of the USA. From Newfoundland, Quebec and Nova Scotia they extend west in a band between the southern tip of Hudson Bay and the Great Lakes, through Ontario,

Manitoba and Saskatchewan to Alberta. In the east of this range many colonies have recently been abandoned and the Common Tern is in long-term decline. Alaska, British Columbia, the North-west Territories and northern Quebec are empty. The break is created by the unsuitable habitat of the Rocky Mountains and the inability of the Common Tern to breed as far north as the Arctic Tern.

More interesting is the lack of nesting Common Terns over the bulk of the USA. There are odd ones in Montana and North Dakota, and a few along the east coast south to North Carolina (where colonies are declining). In the west it is largely replaced by the similar Forster's Tern, although the two do overlap. The total North American population is over 30,000 pairs, but that is not a great many considering the vastness of the range. It sounds a lot, but I often compare these large figures with something more tangible, say a crowd at a football game. Take a 30,000 crowd (not bad) and spread them the length and breadth of a vast continent, and you begin to see that, in reality, it is a small figure.

Farther south, there are very isolated spots on the Common Tern map on the Gulf of Mexico coast, Bermuda, one or two Caribbean islands and the extreme north of South America, but the pattern is not nearly so complete as the Eurasian one.

There are small colonies on keys and islands around Puerto Rico, the US Virgin Islands, the Bahamas and elsewhere in the northern Caribbean and in Gulf County, Florida. There are also regular breeding sites on a few tropical islands, quite exceptional for this cold-temperate breeding species: Aruba, Curaçao, Bonaire, Las Aves, Los Roques and La Orchila. The total Caribbean population is only of the order of five hundred to a thousand pairs.

In the Netherlands Antilles, Common Terns breed on all three islands, the majority on Aruba and the overall total only around two hundred to three hundred pairs. The first breeding record was in 1892, on Bonaire, but breeding was recorded again in 1930 and regularly since 1952 from ten sites on Aruba, four on Curaçao and four on Bonaire, but not all sites are used every year. The breeding habitat is varied, and coral reefs, rocky outcrops, warm sand dunes and even old, disused nest-mounds of flamingos are all adopted as sites for small breeding groups. While some sites maintain their terns over many years – even islets in oil-polluted waters in the harbour of Scottegat, Curaçao – other places, especially saltpans, attract new colonies for short periods. These may be relatively large, with over one hundred pairs.

In Venezuela, Common Terns nest on Los Roques and Las Aves de Barlovento, arriving in May and leaving in July. Some of the breeders may remain in the region all year, but there are also migrants from around September to April, in ones and twos or flocks of up to fifty birds.

In Europe, Common Terns do not nest in Iceland or the Faeroes, although there were brief colonizations of the latter between 1968 and 1974. They do so all along the coast of Norway, right around the North

Cape, and more extensively inland in southern Sweden and around the Baltic coast. They are widespread in Britain and Ireland, least frequent as breeding birds in much of Wales and south-west England. Denmark, the Netherlands and the German coasts (both North Sea and Baltic) have many colonies, but in France the distribution is patchy, mostly confined to Brittany, the Loire valley and the Rhône delta. In north-eastern Italy there are concentrations along the Po.

Iberia is nearly empty of Common Terns, creating a strange gap considering the small but regular breeding colonies in Africa, but there are colonies in western Andalucía and on one or two parts of the Mediterranean coast.

The whole of eastern Europe is dotted with inland concentrations, particularly along the Danube, but the Mediterranean has rather few areas where Common Terns regularly breed. From eastern Europe across Asia as far as Kamchatka, south to the Caspian Sea and Lake Baikal, is a vast area where Common Terns are irregularly scattered. Another area of breeding range covers the uplands of northern Tibet and Mongolia, and there is a broad arc from the Yellow Sea coast south-westwards across central China.

There are scattered colonies around the Persian Gulf and in Iran, and in Turkey, Israel and Tunisia. Common Terns breed in Madeira and the Azores, and in isolated colonies south around the west African coast into the Gulf of Guinea.

In Europe, there are generally stories of decline and contraction of range, with a degree of recovery in recent years as better protection has been enforced in some countries. In Britain and Ireland, there were over 14,700 pairs around the coasts in 1969–70 and there has been little evidence of change since then, although inland populations, which are relatively small, may have increased in Britain but declined in Ireland. It is likely that the 1930s saw the peak numbers of Common Terns breeding in Britain, perhaps before many beaches became increasingly disturbed but after the worst excesses of deliberate exploitation.

In France, the twentieth century saw a decline in fortunes, until just 4500 pairs were estimated by 1976 and only 3000–3500 in 1978. This decline involved a fall of 46 per cent in Brittany between 1970 and 1978 and a decline from 2500–2800 pairs in 1956 to just 1100 pairs in 1979 in the Camargue. Some, but by no means all, declines are associated with persecution in the first two decades of the twentieth century.

Despite the more restricted distribution in Spain, and a decline there too, the Spanish population was thought to be around 11,000 pairs in 1976. In 1980 the largest colony held 2256 pairs, but in 1988 the same one had increased quite dramatically, to 5495 pairs: good news in a story more frequently cataloguing reductions.

In the Netherlands, the story of the Common Tern is remarkable, linked as it is with exploitation for the trade in birds' feathers in the early twentieth century followed by protection, at the eleventh hour, and recovery. Before 1908 there were some 50,000 pairs breeding in the Netherlands. The killing of terns for their feathers brought them almost to extinction in the country, previously one of the great strongholds of the species in the world. Good sense prevailed, but only just in time. Nevertheless, the Common Tern repaid this belated protection by recovering its numbers so well, so quickly, that by 1950 the total was back up to the earlier healthy levels. Sadly, this satisfactory state of affairs did not continue. From 1954 to 1957 the numbers halved, to between 21,500 and 26,000 pairs. The slump continued: in 1971 just about 8000 pairs nested, although 1978 saw a better year, with 10,000 pairs or more.

West Germany had some 6000 pairs breeding in the 1980s. In the 1930s, terns had declined inland, but coastal colonies still totalled about 10,000 pairs, perhaps more. The decline inland became a more general one through the 1950s and 1960s. Meanwhile, in Denmark, numbers fluctuated but not by much: the population has always been relatively small, at around six to eight hundred pairs.

Norway and Sweden include tern areas *par excellence*, and both countries have substantial populations of great importance. In 1970 there were around 13,000 pairs in Norway. In Sweden, a few years later, the total was estimated at 40,000 pairs, the only national total recently to approach the once great numbers of the Netherlands.

Finland has seen a slow, irregular decline in some parts, while numbers have held their own in others: overall the total remains around a relatively modest 6000 pairs. In Estonia, about 3000 pairs bred in 1965, increasing to 5000 pairs through the mid-1970s. There are over a thousand pairs in Latvia, and Poland has 2000 pairs, completing the strong presence around the whole of the Baltic.

In eastern Europe, there are small numbers in many places but a long-term decline is evident. In European Russia, colonies are scattered but concentrations of some 14,000 pairs around the Black Sea and 4000 pairs on the Sea of Azov were known in the early 1980s. Turkey has some sizeable colonies but recent information is sparse; a few thousand pairs all told is the best that can be expected.

In the Azores, Common Terns were once described as abundant, but a decrease is almost certain, prompted by greater disturbance of the nesting beaches and islands. The Azores has become the focus of much tern study in recent years, as the Roseate Tern numbers have crashed catastrophically elsewhere and the Azores population has increased in importance.

Up to nine hundred pairs of Common Terns bred in Mauritania in the early 1960s, but by 1974 there were just 185 pairs left on the Banc d'Arguin, but this colony is probably subject to frequent fluctuations. Some breed in Liberia and south-east Tunisia and erratically in Western Sahara, at Puerto Cansado. In Senegambia, the Saloum delta is a breeding locality, as are the Bijagos Islands of Guinea-Bissau and the Dodo estuary in Nigeria. These West African breeding groups, though, are always quite small and rather erratic, but do represent a remarkable southward extension into what are more usually considered the wintering areas of terns from Europe.

Distribution in Britain and Ireland

In the 1968–72 breeding bird atlas fieldwork throughout Britain and Ireland, Common Terns were recorded as possibly breeding in 256 10-km squares (although many of these simply had a bird or two present in the breeding season), and probably breeding in 81 squares. They were confirmed as having bred in 556 squares, the number of squares in total (893) being 23 per cent of all the 10-km squares in the National Grid. For a shoreline bird, that is a respectably high score (the Arctic Tern, for example, being recorded from just 14 per cent of all squares, with confirmed breeding from 413).

The distribution was markedly biased towards Scotland and the whole Irish coast, with other concentrations on Anglesey (and to a lesser extent around Liverpool Bay), the Dorset and Hampshire coast, the Greater Thames (North Kent and Essex) and around East Anglia. In Scotland, central Ireland and in the East Midlands and East Anglia, there is a substantial scatter of dots inland, totalling around 150 10-km squares in the three categories of possible, probable and confirmed breeding. The total population estimated in *The Atlas of Breeding Birds in Britain and Ireland*, published in 1976, was between 15,000 and 20,000 pairs.

In Scotland, the distribution of breeding Common Terns is widespread and quite even around the mainland coasts and also covering most of the Inner and Outer Hebrides, Orkney and Shetland. Scotland supports around a quarter of the British and Irish total, but most of the colonies are small, with just one regularly holding more than five hundred pairs. Inland nesting is most frequent in the east, where shallow waters for fishing and extensive riverside shingle for nesting are more available.

Counts in Shetland and the Outer Hebrides in the 1980s indicated a much higher number than had previously been estimated (a thousand pairs and six hundred pairs, respectively). In Shetland, about four times as many colonies were found in 1980 as in census work in 1969–70, but the average was just twelve pairs. Only one Shetland colony held one hundred or more pairs. On Fair Isle, Common Terns bred for the first time in 1970, one pair on the Stack o' North Haven. A pair bred again in 1972, and the colony developed to about fifty pairs in 1982.

It was only in the 1970s that the plumages of Common, Arctic and Roseate Terns were separated.

Common Tern
(backlit)

Arctic Tern
(backlit)

Arctic Tern
(breeding ad.)

Common Tern
(breeding ad.)

Common Tern
(juv.)

Roseate Tern
(breeding ad.)

Arctic Tern
(juv.)

Roseate Tern
(juv.)

Common Tern
(first-summer *'portlandica'*)

Norman Arlott

Fluctuations since have taken the colony to a high of 59 pairs in 1988 and a low of just seven in 1990. The productivity in later years was disastrously low.

Few west-coast colonies in Scotland hold more than fifty pairs. Typically, the terns are widely scattered in small groups, rather than congregating into very large colonies. In the east, colonies of one hundred or more pairs are found between the Moray Basin and East Lothian, with the largest being those on the Aberdeen and Lothian coasts and the Forth islands. These colonies fluctuate widely, typical of the fickle terns (although it is the Sandwich Tern that is most readily brought to mind in this respect, being the species most likely to desert mid-season and move elsewhere the next).

The Sands of Forvie colony reached a peak of 1200 in 1958 but declined as Black-headed Gulls and Sandwich Terns increased on the dunes. The Isle of May once had a magnificent colony, as many as 5000 or 6000 pairs nesting in 1946–47, which was really exceptional. There was a calamitous decline soon afterwards, and by 1957 the ternery had gone altogether. Later, gulls were controlled there, but it was not until 1980 that a pair of Common Terns bred successfully again on the May.

Tentsmuir formerly held large numbers but was practically abandoned during the war years of 1939–45 because of excessive disturbance. Numbers never recovered, and the odd pairs that have tried nesting since then have often fared badly because of flooding. At Strathbeg, north of Aberdeen, between seventy and 170 pairs bred between 1975 and 1983; at Aberlady in East Lothian, numbers fluctuated between 75 and 318 pairs from 1969 to 1983, with a gradual decline matched by an increase in Arctic Terns. Inchmickery, a small island in the Firth of Forth, has a fine colony, sometimes down to one hundred pairs but with as many as 750 in the 1970s.

Irish Common Tern colonies follow the usual trend of 'little and often', with small groups widely scattered. They nest around most of the coast, and inland are particularly concentrated on Lough Neagh, the Shannon lakes, on the lakes of Connemara and around Lough Erne in Fermanagh.

On the coast, this was the commonest tern in the east in the 1950s, with Common Terns outnumbering Arctics thirteen to one in Down, whereas Arctics had exceeded Commons there in the nineteenth century. In Dublin, a colony at Malahide totalled several thousand pairs of terns early in the twentieth century and the Common Tern was by far the more numerous species. In Wexford, Arctic Terns outnumbered Commons in 1934, but by the 1950s it was the Common Tern that accounted for more than half of the breeding pairs. By the 1960s, Common Terns there outnumbered Arctics by at least five to one. On the Galway and Donegal coasts, however, Arctics predominated, leaving the Common Tern to dominate the colonies inland.

In the 1969–70 seabird census (in which I was pleased to take part in County Mayo and Connemara, visiting a number of wonderful headlands and beaches with scatterings of breeding terns), Common Terns outnumbered identified Arctics in Ireland by 2·8 to one but, sadly, so many went unidentified that the true position is impossible to specify. Nevertheless, by 1984 Common Terns on the coast had, generally, substantially declined. In part this was due to the abandonment of Tern Island, a large colony in Wexford Harbour where there were 850 pairs in 1969. The birds from this colony may have moved over to the colonies of western Britain (a situation reversed by the abandonment of British colonies of Roseate Terns in 1991, in favour of Irish ones). All the same, many other colonies declined. In Cork and Kerry there used to be many small and medium sized colonies; now there are fewer small ones, and hardly any of substantial size. The reasons for this decline are unknown.

Despite its delicate, lightweight appearance, the Common Tern is a powerful flier.

In England, the Common Tern is a bird that has long been linked with Norfolk, where the broad shingle beaches, extensive saltmarshes, dune systems and abundance of tidal creeks make ideal tern territory. World War II encouraged terns to nest on mined (and therefore undisturbed) beaches at Yarmouth. After the war, the terns moved to Scroby Sands, first nesting there in 1947 (a period of real excitement on the East Anglian coast, with returning Avocets to guard, too). By 1948, 370 pairs nested, but high tides and storms limited breeding success. In most years, until 1965, between 150 and 250 pairs nested.

Blakeney Point is a tremendous sweep of shingle from Cley beach westwards across the mouth of Blakeney Harbour. It is a brilliant place for birds, not least the rare and exotic migrants that make landfall there in spring and autumn. Its breeding terns now concentrate in a reserve

Sandy beaches and dunes make classic nesting sites in eastern England.

area, suitably roped off and well protected, close to the extreme point. As long ago as 1830 breeding terns were noted there, and by 1935 the colony was at its height, in the period of greatest prosperity for Common Terns in the United Kingdom. In the late 1930s and again in the early 1950s, up to 2000 pairs bred. Since then the colony continued to be large and dramatic for some years, but more usually between 950 and 1500 pairs settled each spring. In 1969 there were 1200 pairs, but by 1986 the total had declined to 275. By 1989, just 240 pairs bred, with little success because of Herring Gull predation.

Another great centre for terns in Norfolk is Scolt Head. Nesting began in 1922 with just seventeen pairs, a small acorn which soon sprouted into the great oak of 1300 pairs by about 1925. In 1938 the colony peaked at 2470 pairs, one of the greatest Common Tern colonies in the world. Up to 1958 numbers held up well, with nine hundred to 1400 pairs breeding, but a decline set in, with only a brief recovery (to nine hundred pairs in 1961), and between four hundred and six hundred pairs became the norm. In 1969 there were still five hundred pairs but between 1985 and 1989 annual totals rarely exceeded two hundred, hitting a miserably low point in 1989 when just 159 pairs reared a mere ten young between them. Fox predation was particularly heavy that year, but then, there have always been foxes.

Other coastal sites in Norfolk include Cley, Salthouse, Stiffkey, Holme and Snettisham. At Snettisham numbers varied between 130 and eighty between 1985 and 1989.

At Breydon Water, Common Terns nest on specially provided platforms. From 58 pairs in 1985, numbers rose steadily to 95 in 1989. This is a welcome bright spot in a county whose terns have hit a depressingly dark period in their history. From 2000 pairs in Norfolk as a whole in 1969, the county total declined to 718 by 1988. Inland, the Broads attract small groups, with up to 35 pairs (on special rafts) on Ranworth Broad and smaller groups at Ormesby and Hickling.

The sad decline in Norfolk has been repeated in Suffolk. The situation is, if anything, even more strange and worrying. In the early 1970s, there were regularly four hundred pairs at Minsmere and forty at Havergate Island. In 1984 Minsmere had a pathetic remnant, of just fifteen pairs, and in 1987 just a single pair nested there on the famous Scrape. Numbers in the county were at an all-time low in 1986, but in 1987 at least Havergate showed a good revival, with 79 breeding pairs. Other sites – the Stour and Walberswick – have a mere handful.

Another good tern county is Kent, where 'very large numbers' were once reported to breed at Dungeness (the shingle beach that beats all shingle beaches for size), although by 1907 the colony there had declined to just two hundred pairs. By the 1930s there was a big increase, in line with many other coastal sites in England about that time, and the Common Terns had become concentrated in a strip of beach just 200 m by 1500 m in extent. From 1500 pairs, numbers declined seriously with increased military activity in the war years, and the great ternery was abandoned. About fifty pairs continued to breed, scattered all over the area in small clusters. Rye Harbour and Pett Level in Sussex benefited from this, as many of the terns from Dungeness moved there.

None bred at all at Dungeness between 1956 and 1960, a sad state of affairs for what had become, briefly, one of the premier terneries in Europe. After 1964, however, up to two hundred pairs regularly bred. In 1976, the terns switched to islands in the new gravel pits in the beach and subsequently allowed to flood, and 245 pairs bred that year.

In the Swale, a variety of islands, large and small, have been colonized by Common Terns. There were 213 pairs in 1955 after a period of steady increase, then 250 pairs on Fowey Island alone in 1965. Fowey was later deserted, however, and the Swale terns have declined to a small echo of their former glories.

The Medway Islands have also seen a story of rise and fall, with 683 pairs by 1955, principally on Nor, Bee and Stoke islands, 331 in 1961 and a mere 87 by 1972. Cliffe Pools saw the first breeding of Common Terns on the Thames in Kent, in 1958, and the colony rose to two hundred pairs at times in the 1960s, but there has been a marked decline since.

Across the Thames, in Essex, Common Terns reached a record level in 1981, with 278 breeding pairs. This was largely due to the establishment of a thriving colony on Foulness Island, which rose from 61 pairs in 1972 to 182 pairs in 1981. In the past, Horsey Island, with 120 pairs in 1953, had accounted for most of the Common Terns nesting in Essex. The traditional north Essex saltmarsh colonies had little success in the 1970s and 1980s, and Common Terns took increasingly to artificial sites inland. Abberton reservoir had tempted up to forty pairs in the early 1950s in somewhat exceptional conditions, and when, in 1980, a raft was provided for terns to nest on, fifteen pairs quickly accepted the challenge and did so. In 1982 there were 28 pairs on the raft, conveniently placed close to a hide so that many people could enjoy the spectacle. In 1967, thirty pairs bred at Hanningfield reservoir and Heybridge gravel pits have since attracted up to 35 pairs.

Hampshire is a county whose coast has regularly echoed to the cries of breeding terns and Black-headed Gulls. In 1987 over three hundred pairs of Common Terns bred at Needs Ore Point, at the mouth of the Beaulieu estuary. The colony there declined to 156 pairs in 1990. Meanwhile, Langstone Harbour maintained between 45 and 74 pairs in this period, and between Pitts Deep and Hurst up to sixty pairs bred. It is not a county whose Common Tern numbers make dramatic reading, after all.

There is little point here going on to catalogue the tern colonies of the whole British coast. Suffice it to say that these examples so far quoted are enough to give the flavour of erratic rise and fall, displacement by disturbance, encouragement by a lack of disturbance brought about by wartime activities or coastal defences, some mysterious disappearances even of thriving colonies that seemed set to go on for ever, and a move to the new habitats made available inland. Terns have always been like that. Even fine reserves like Minsmere, where the terns are cosseted and fussed over all summer long, have failed to hold on to them for ever.

The establishment (albeit with some fits and starts) of breeding at reservoirs and gravel pits is perhaps the chief point of interest in recent years. One more example of this is the situation in the West Midlands, an area as far from the sea as is possible in England. Breeding was first reported in 1952, on a flooded gravel pit near Burton-on-Trent in Staffordshire. Common Terns bred there in most subsequent years, although never more than three pairs. Another gravel pit nearby attracted a pair or two, while in north Warwickshire another complex of flooded pits and islands was colonized in 1969, with varying success. In 1981, twelve pairs raised 37 flying young, as good a performance as might be expected from any inland site. By 1986, at least forty adults could be seen there and thirty young were raised. In 1987 numbers reached a new high, with twenty pairs fledging 56 young and post-breeding flocks of seventy or so birds on a regular basis. In that year the first breeding attempt was made in the county of West Midlands itself. Human, avian and mammalian predators, disturbance, flooding and habitat changes all account for nesting failures at the regular midland sites and at those that are used occasionally.

In line with many inland areas, the West Midland Common Terns appear to feed their chicks on small fish, while the many migrants over lakes and reservoirs there generally feed on flying insects, especially midges, and rarely plunge-dive as they do on the coast.

Apart from the breeding population of Britain and Ireland, Common Terns are, of course, widespread as migrants in spring, late summer and autumn. Almost any coastal locality will see a tern or two fly by at these times. They move by at headlands, or pause for a while on estuarine sand bars and secluded beaches. Favoured places include shallow, sandy estuaries where clear water allows a sight of plentiful small fish.

I well remember watching flocks of several thousand terns at the mouth of the Dee, on the England–Wales border, in August. This seems to be an important gathering ground after the breeding season, presumably drawing birds from far afield, perhaps many from Scotland as well as north-west England, and Wales. Morecambe Bay is similarly favoured by terns that disperse after breeding, or are on their way south later in the autumn. These big flocks are excitable and fascinating to watch and are, of course, likely to be mixed with Arctic, Sandwich and Little Terns and even attract the occasional family group of Roseates or migrant Black Terns as well.

On the east coast of England, Common Terns are indeed common in most places in late summer and autumn. In the north-east and off such well-watched headlands as Flamborough Head and Filey Brigg they are often about, feeding or in determined movements offshore.

Norfolk is always a good place to watch them, whether from the sandy beaches at Holme, Holkham or Wells-next-the-Sea, the shingle of Blakeney Point and Cley or the cliffs of Hunstanton and Sheringham. They are often around Blakeney, Cley and Salthouse in sizeable numbers, moving up and down the beach in family groups or small flocks and resting on the lagoons just inside the massive shingle banks. Farther south, Common Terns are always to be found on the Suffolk coastal lagoons such as Benacre and at Minsmere, where the artificial scrape on the RSPB reserve has often been a major collecting point for both breeding and migrating terns.

In Essex coastal flocks are generally small, but there are reports of up to 550 in May and 3000 in September. On around the headlands of Kent and the estuaries of the south coast the situation is much the same, with regular gatherings of anything from half a dozen to a hundred or two and occasionally much bigger flocks.

In Scotland, the great eastern firths often have flocks of 2000–3000 in autumn, an irresistible attraction for passing Arctic Skuas. In Ireland there are great assemblies on the coasts of Dublin and Wicklow in autumn, with a nocturnal roost at Sandymount Strand in Dublin Bay. The birds feed 10 km offshore on the India Bank and return at dusk, often swirling around in vast flocks more like congregations of waders than terns, performing all manner of aerobatic manoeuvres before settling in for the night. These flocks, mainly of adult birds, remain from July into September, and regularly involve 4000 birds, with at least 7000 at times in 1983. Sometimes other flocks of up to five hundred gather off the east Cork coast at about the same time.

Inland in England, Common Terns are regular migrants at lakes, reservoirs and flooded pits in April and May and again from July to late September. In Rutland, for example, the earliest report was on 18 April, the latest on 17 October, and the largest flock of 21 birds, in spring. In the West Midlands, between 1929 and 1978, 2400 Common Terns were reported (compared with 2173 Arctics): the earliest date was 4 April, the peak spring movement being in May, and the latest date was a somewhat exceptional 3 November (the usual autumn passage being largely over by mid-September). Only five flocks in all those years exceeded twenty birds (compared with eighteen of Arctics), and the biggest party was 45, in May.

In recent years, with greatly increased coverage of most waters in the region compared with the early part of the period analysed above, the numbers of Common Terns to be seen exceed those that might be expected from these figures, but locally-breeding birds blur the picture. In Cambridgeshire, numbers in recent years at Grafham Water have clearly been increased by local breeding stock, and up to one hundred or more Common Terns can sometimes be seen loafing about on the reservoir buoys and rafts in early autumn. Judging by the preponderance of moulting adults, these may be mostly birds that have attempted to breed inland in eastern England and failed, for one reason or another, and then simply idle away the days until they have to move south. Certainly the Grafham flocks seem to have little real aim in life and it is hard to decide just what they are, or have been, doing.

Inland, Arctic Terns tend to come through in a more concentrated passage, sometimes in much bigger numbers, than Common Terns in spring. It would be interesting to study their behaviour more carefully. Although Common Terns often congregate on some feature – be it a water-skiers' raft or a collection of buoys, or a fisherman's boat – they

In West Africa, mixed flocks of terns gather in quite different environments from their usual European surroundings.

spend much of the time dispersed around a reservoir, feeding in ones and twos and seemingly acting quite independently except for their co-ordinated arrival and departure. Arctics, unless they are in the occasional very big flocks that turn up for an hour or two and then move on, seem to keep together in more coherent groups, even feeding in parties of six or eight or more at a time and moving around the reservoir in a bunch. This, though, is little more than a vague impression, and needs checking, but certainly Common Terns, although gregarious, sociable creatures, are generally widely dispersed when feeding over the larger lakes and reservoirs inland.

The picture that emerges from this brief look at the status of Common Terns in Britain and Ireland shows that this species can be expected between spring and autumn on practically any coast and that any birdwatcher regularly visiting waterside localities inland in May, or August and September, should expect to see a few terns, and maybe a small flock on most visits.

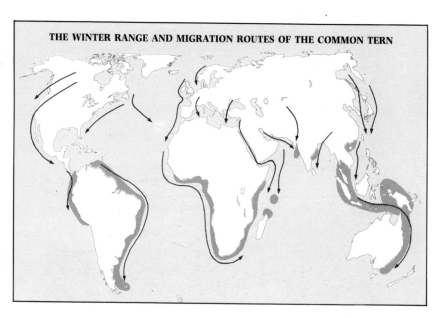

THE WINTER RANGE AND MIGRATION ROUTES OF THE COMMON TERN

Winter distribution and migration

Common Terns are migratory almost throughout their Palearctic and Nearctic ranges. A few winter in Portuguese and Spanish waters, but most Western Palearctic terns move south to spend the winter around Africa.

In winter, Common Terns may be found practically anywhere around the enormous coastline of Africa, from the Nile delta around to the Red Sea. Birds from the Palearctic begin to appear from late August to October, and remain until March or April.

A number of bird species of widespread distribution in Europe show, when fully studied by ringing, that populations from particular parts of Europe maintain discrete wintering grounds. For example, British Swallows spend the winter in extreme southern Africa, while German ones concentrate a little farther north, keeping quite separate. It is much the same with Common Terns, if not so strongly marked.

Common Terns breeding in southern and western Europe tend to stay north of the equator in winter, while those from the north and east go farther south, entailing a very much longer migration every spring and autumn. Individuals ringed in Great Britain have been recovered in Morocco, Algeria, Western Sahara, Mauritania, Senegambia, Guinea, Sierra Leone, Liberia, Ivory Coast, Ghana, Togo, Benin, Nigeria, Gabon, Angola, Namibia and South Africa. Those from western Germany, Switzerland and westwards to Spain have much the same distribution, centred along the West African coast between 10° and 20°N. Common Terns from eastern Germany, Russia and Scandinavia travel as far as Angola and South Africa, even Mozambique. While many northern birds remain in Ghana, those from western Germany, Finland and Estonia, and smaller numbers from Sweden and Denmark, reach South Africa.

One individual, ringed as a chick in Sweden, was evidently caught up in a strong westerly airstream around the Cape and, still only six months old, was found in Fremantle, Western Australia. An Irish bird has also been recovered in Australia, in Victoria, after a really remarkable journey.

After breeding, British Common Terns have a leisurely dispersal as if in no particular hurry to move south. In fact, some go a short way to the north, although by September all are headed south and in October they are going on through Biscay and around Iberia. By November, there is a rapid southward movement along the West African coast, and few are north of 20°N. In December, most are in Ghana and along the coasts of Sierra Leone and Liberia.

Central European birds face a problem in autumn, as they have to cross, or get around, the barrier of the Alps. Some seem to fly right over the top in Switzerland, but there is a concentration along the Rhône valley and it is highly probable that large lakes and river valleys provide 'easy' routes through the mountains. Breeding birds from Hungary move south to the Balkans and, along with those from the Black Sea, fly westwards along the Mediterranean to exit via Gibraltar, and then turn south. A few Black Sea breeders, however, remain to spend the winter around Turkey.

In Ghana, terns are trapped by children, for fun. Common Terns are frequently caught and this adds a bias to the ringing recoveries (although, as many rings are kept as ornaments and never reported, the apparent concentration in Ghana is probably genuine and little overstated).

Wintering Common Terns visit such 'paradise' islands as the Seychelles.

Once the adults have returned north in spring, the African coast is populated only by immature terns except for the isolated breeding colonies. First-summer birds (that is one-year-olds) spend the year between 10° and 20°N. They remain in West Africa for the following winter and spring, but many then move north in summer and some reach Britain by about late June or July. The occasional exception, a young bird reaching Britain instead of staying behind in Africa in summer, provides the *'portlandica* tern' phenomenon that so puzzled people in England in the 1950s and 1960s.

In East Africa, Common Terns of uncertain origin appear on passage in Egypt and, while numbers are small in the Red Sea, they are abundant (sometimes in flocks of thousands of birds) in Somalia. Kenya has large flocks and probably these are of the Tibetan race. Two birds recovered in Somalia, however, had been ringed on the Black Sea at Odessa. In Tanzania, where the Common Tern is regularly seen on the coast, individuals have been recovered wearing rings from Austria and Germany, but it is surmised that these simply followed the west coast of Africa and turned north around the Cape of Good Hope.

It may be that an inland passage over north-eastern Africa, especially along the Rift Valley, is regular. An airstrike added the little extra piece of knowledge that at least one group of unfortunate Common Terns met its end while flying inland over the Sudan in late October, and a two-year-old bird recovered on the Nile in Sudan had had a ring placed on its leg in Norway. On the Rift Valley lakes in Kenya and Burundi, Common Terns are more or less annual in appearance.

In Israel, the species is common on migration in spring at Eilat, the splendid birdwatching centre at the head of the Gulf of Aqaba on the Red Sea. Here Common Terns may be watched flying over the sea in company with White-eyed Gulls, Brown Boobies, the occasional Caspian Tern and Great Black-headed Gull and even, now and then, a similar White-cheeked Tern or two. Many that winter in the Persian Gulf are probably from central Asia. Ringed birds from Turkmeniya and Novosibirsk recovered in October and January on the south Caspian Sea may have been wintering there, or may have been on their way to the Gulf. Central Asian breeders also move to the coasts of Pakistan, India and Sri Lanka in winter.

The south-east Asian race, *tibetana*, probably winters mainly on the east coast of India and around the convoluted coasts of Burma and Malaysia, while the east Siberian birds, of the race *longipennis*, winter from peninsular Malaysia throughout Indonesia and New Guinea and even south around the eastern coast of Australia. What magical places these eastern Common Terns must visit!

In Japan, the Common Tern is common, sometimes quite abundant locally, along both the Pacific and Sea of Japan coasts. There is a northwards movement in May and early June. Large flocks appear suddenly inland in southern Hokkaido in May, and again between late August and October. The main autumn migration, however, is in September. Common Terns are then common along the Okhotsk Sea coasts and on nearby inland lakes and some reach the Inland Sea in September. In 1920, a flock of 1500 was reported as late as 18 November in Toyama-ken. These Japanese birds are of the race *longipennis* (with a few apparently from the *minussensis* group if that race is a genuine one). The race *longipennis* breeds as close as the Kurile Islands and is regarded as a potential discovery as a breeding bird in Japan.

In the New World, Common Terns appear outside the breeding season on the west coast of America, chiefly on the California coast, and south-wards along the Pacific coast of Central America and on as far as about Lima, Peru. On the east side of America, they are found along coastal waters and well out into the Atlantic, around the whole of the Gulf of Mexico and the West Indies coasts, and around the Atlantic coast of South America to the Gulf of San Jorge and, once, even in the Falkland Islands. A Common Tern recovered in December on the Ivory Coast had been ringed in New York; one ringed as a chick in Massachusetts was recovered in October in the Azores, and another ringed on the Great Lakes was found in the Atlantic close to the Azores. How much this represents a regular easterly drift, or simply reflects a few individuals caught up in severe weather and carried across the Atlantic, is not certain.

5

FOOD AND FEEDING

EVERYONE knows that terns eat fish. End of chapter. There are, of course, people who look a bit deeper than that, and the precise nature of the diet of the Common Tern, at all times of the year, has been well studied. More than that, the way in which it captures its prey, and the success rate of its hunting in different conditions, have been the subject of quite detailed work by a few dedicated and accurate researchers.

Food dictates a good deal of the life of any bird. Clearly no bird can live in an area where it cannot feed, and the more adaptable a bird is in terms of its food and feeding habits, the more flexible it can be in exploiting a variety of environments and geographical areas. If a species is tied down specifically to eating one kind of food, in one particular way, it is very much more restricted in its options. Examples of the opportunist, omnivorous type include House Sparrows and Herring Gulls, while specialists that are really well adapted to particular foods but ill-fitted to eat anything else are birds such as flamingos, skimmers and treecreepers. The Common Tern is somewhere between the two extremes.

Overall, the Common Tern as a species eats chiefly marine fish, but it is, within that basic role, an opportunist. Changing circumstances dictate changes in the type of prey taken and the way in which it is caught. Studies have shown that some colonies subsist largely on fish, while others rely much more on crustaceans. A colony at one particular site may eat mostly one kind of fish in one year, but switch, through force of circumstance, to a different prey species the next. Even from day to day, or hour to hour, the feeding patterns and preferred prey may change.

Nevertheless, the Common Tern is basically equipped to take on small fish which it catches, in its bill, close to the surface. This first of all requires that the fish can be seen from the air, and therefore demands clear water (to a point: I often wonder how any tern can see and catch fish in the murky waters of the North Sea on a windy autumn day).

Terns do not, as a rule, feed like kingfishers, by perching and watching, although some occasionally, and a few individuals more persistently, do dive from fixed perches on bridges or moored boats. Usually terns search for prey by flying over the water, peering down as they go. It is quite easy to see the tilted head, bill pointing downwards, as a tern is actively searching for something to catch. Once something has been spotted, the tern pauses in its flight and dives in, head-first.

Common Terns frequently hover before plunging. The usual height is between 1 and 6 m, and various studies have shown that the average height of a dive is quite low, about 3 m. Often the tern dives right under, briefly fully immersed, but rarely penetrates more than 50 cm below the surface. They are what is known as 'superficial plunge divers'.

Many dives end in a splash, or more accurately a splat, a noisy smack against the surface which raises little or no water or spray. They are indeed often rather superficial plunges, with wings and tail still showing above the surface, depending on the depth of the prey. If the tern submerges completely, it does so only for a brief moment: one study of 164 dives gave an average length of 1·1 seconds, another of 213 dives produced an average of 0·8 seconds underwater. The maximum is just 1·6 seconds and, short though that is, if you close your eyes and imagine it, it seems to be considerably longer than the usual 'instant' splash and recovery that is so familiar to the seaside birdwatcher.

The plunge for fish requires a sharp eye, and rapid reflexes to co-ordinate wing, body and tail movements.

The long outer tail feathers, or streamers, which give the Common Tern such an air of elegance, are actually probably used in adjusting the angle of dive, allowing accurate, small changes during the descent so that the bird makes a successful strike. Other birds with forked tails – Red Kites, frigatebirds, swallows and so on – also use the tail as a rudder in this way. The extreme development of the flexible, elegant streamers on a tern's tail, however (think especially of the lovely Roseate Tern) may well be more than is strictly needed to perform this function and doubles up as a feature in the bird's displays. It is not so much the streamer that helps in the aerobatics, but the long, pointed outer edge of a forked or triangular tail clearly gives a greater surface area to act as a rudder when the tail is twisted than would the short edge of a rounded one.

The fish is captured in the bill and brought to the surface, either to be swallowed or to be carried off to impress and feed the bird's mate or to feed its hungry young. The bill of a Common Tern is about 35–40 mm long, and sharply pointed. It is, nevertheless, quite a stout and substantial affair, a good dagger-shape rather than a stiletto. I once drew some Common and Arctic Terns to illustrate an identification paper, and the drawings were returned because I had, said the editor, made the bills too thick. Probably I had (it's the kind of thing I usually do), but they are the kind of beaks that make descriptions potentially confusing. True, they are long and slender: but look at a close-up photograph (or the real thing) and you will see that they can equally be described as stout, robust pieces of equipment, long and heavy enough to make some small gulls' beaks look insubstantial. It is all relative. Anyway, the bill of a tern is a suitably strong, sharp-edged tool for dealing with small, wriggling, slippery, muscular fish, but, like the Grey Heron, the tern is a grabber not a stabber.

Once a fish is grasped, it is held in the bill tip, usually neatly grasped by the narrow section between the gills. I have not checked, but the Marples, in their excellent book, claimed that all terns usually seem to hold a fish hanging down on the left side. That sounds an unlikely tale, but they would not have just made it up. The fish is dextrously turned head-first into the mouth and quickly swallowed with hardly any noticeable backward jerk of the head to start it on its way.

Occasionally a tern can manage to grasp and carry two or more fish at a time, but it does not have the ability to use bill and tongue together to collect a whole beakful of fish like a Puffin does. At breeding colonies where terns frequently carry fish, 1·7 per cent of those counted with fish in the bill had more than one fish, some even as many as five sandeels.

The rate of diving and the precise nature of the hunting activity vary according to the abundance (or more precisely, density), depth in the water and size of the prey. If there is a low density of prey the Common Tern moves around quickly, searching large areas in a determined way. If there is a greater density of prey available, the terns seem more excitable, changing direction and turning back on their tracks much more frequently, searching more slowly and more often flying into the wind to allow a slower movement over the water. The impression is one of a more thorough search of small areas, rather than a rapid coverage of large areas of water until something happens to be detected.

Where food is plentiful, Common Terns gather to feed together and often plunge almost simultaneously.

One of the simpler things to note is the success rate of diving birds, but interpretation of the results is not so easy. The success depends on the visibility of the prey, the size of the fish, the abundance of fish and the depth at which the fish are swimming. Then you must add in the individual skill (perhaps) and age (which affects the experience) of the bird. Only if these factors can be properly determined are counts of successful dives of much value.

Studies on the Ythan estuary in eastern Scotland showed that capture rates also varied according to wind speed. Including aborted dives as 'failures' as well as plunges that produced no fish, the success rate declined by 0·2 prey items per minute for every 16 km per hour rise in wind speed. Wind first ruffles and then breaks up the water surface, reducing the visibility of fish, and perhaps making the controlled dive necessary for accuracy more difficult. In stronger winds, the Ythan terns deliberately sought more sheltered places in which to fish. Gales make feeding particularly difficult, and it has been shown that chicks are fed less often during strong winds.

The effect of wind is not so simply determined, however, as in the open sea it seems that a moderate wind is better for feeding terns than either a flat calm or a gale. In studies made in moderate conditions, 39 per cent of dives were complete, and terns dived on average 1·5 times per minute, capturing prey 0·5 times per minute. In calm seas, only 22 per cent of dives were followed through, at a rate of just 1·0 per minute, and prey was captured only 0·23 times per minute. Quite why this should be so is not so easy to explain and the problems of increased availability of prey, or increased visibility of larger fish, or fish closer to the surface, have to be disentangled from the simple variations in wind and water surface-conditions. Rough water makes fish-spotting more difficult; calm air may make flying, hovering and diving more energy-consuming and less efficient.

Off the Ghana coast in winter terns gather to feed around fishing boats as they haul their nets.

Terns watched by Euan Dunn as they fed over submerged reefs and sandbanks captured more prey at low tide than at high tide. Other studies have shown that more food is carried to the breeding colony at low tide, or as the tide is falling, than at high tide. But the local situation overrides many of the observed average patterns.

In estuaries, marine fish move upriver on a rising tide and thus become more available to the terns. Rather than doing best at low tide, they improve their fishing as the tide comes in. On the Ythan, fishing success was best on rising spring tides, with prey caught at a rate of 0·66 items per minute, compared with 0·12 items per minute on neap tides.

Where there is a shoal of fish close to the surface, the general flurry and excitement of gleaming white birds diving in and raising equally gleaming white splashes attracts more terns from far and wide. Then the diving rates increase and fishing success is improved. Euan Dunn showed that flocks of Common Terns had a success rate of 40–57 per cent compared with the 27–44 per cent of solitary birds watched on the same occasions. Does being in a flock improve fishing success, or does increased success attract the flock?

The white element of the plumage of many seabirds – Gannets, for example – is likely to be an aid to fishing, as diving individuals can be seen from a great distance by others, which then move towards a successful bird and are, in their turn, also observed by others which follow them in. Like vultures gathering at a carcass, apparently 'appearing from nowhere', the 'extended flock' of terns can home in on a shoal of fish in double-quick time, the white arrows of diving terns serving as markers to the easy prey.

There are other methods of feeding used by Common Terns, in addition to the typical plunge-diving. They often simply dip down in flight to pick something from the water surface. At the Ythan, where the terns are particularly well studied, increased wind-speed and associated wave size stimulated a gradual change from diving to surface-dipping, especially for sandeels, and this became more successful than plunging. In winter, off West Africa, Common Terns dip for food from within seine nets being raised by fishermen, and they also pick up small fish driven to the surface by predatory tuna beneath. Fish on or close to the beach are sometimes picked up, a fact which children in West Africa exploit, to catch terns in baited snares lying on the sand. This species has also been seen walking about on the shore and picking up prey items.

When over fresh water, Common Terns often dip to feed, rather than plunging, and this is especially noticeable with migrant terns over reservoirs. These, and breeding birds near the coast, also catch insects in the air, like giant Swallows. They are quite adept at aerial feeding, and there are also a number of reports of Common Terns 'playing' with objects caught on the wind and carried up in the air.

If there is a food shortage when the demands of the chicks at a colony are greatest, Common Terns may also resort to chasing and robbing other Common Terns or terns of a different species. The moment when a fish is offered to a chick is frequently the most dangerous, when another tern is most likely to nip in and steal the food from the mouth of the hungry but fumbling youngster.

What, exactly, are these diving terns eating? Small herrings, sprats, sandeels and a variety of other common marine fish make up quite a varied fishy diet. Almost anything of suitable size will do: pollack, haddock, whiting, cod, mackerel and sticklebacks are all frequently taken, for example. Some stranger fish are sometimes caught: lumpsucker (by no means the thin, silvery slip of a fish that we usually think of as tern prey), small flatfish and gurnards, for instance.

Small fish form the principal food of Common Terns.

In suitable seas, anchovies are regularly caught, both in the Americas and off the African coast. In Ghana, sardines are important in the terns' diet. The availability of suitable fish determines the migration routes in such waters. In autumn, dense flocks of terns migrate through the Gulf of Guinea in a narrow belt of inshore water, within 22 km of the shore. Sardines are really abundant in this area at that time of year. In spring, the sardines move farther out to sea, and the terns are not seen in the inshore area and must be sought much farther out, where the food is.

Inland, Common Terns take small fish from rivers and reservoirs, including practically all the common species that may be expected. Roach, perch, ruffe, bleak, tiny bream, rudd, minnows and even goldfish are all in the long list of freshwater food. Salmon and trout appear, too, but fortunately for the terns, unlike Goosanders, Red-breasted Mergansers and Cormorants, no-one has yet seriously complained that they ruin salmonid stocks.

The average length of the fish caught was about 5·5 cm in one study, 7·5 cm in another. Small chicks are fed smaller prey than larger ones, although often a fish fed to a chick seems grossly oversized. At least one careful study showed that fishing terns ate smaller fish than they took back to feed to their mates and young. This is described more fully in later chapters and, in the case of courtship feeding, is related to the need of the female to build up sufficient reserves to enable her to form a clutch of large, energy-rich eggs.

Common Terns suffered from food shortages in Shetland and elsewhere in the 1980s, as did the more abundant Arctic Terns but to a lesser extent. With too few sandeels to feed to their chicks, Arctic Terns, Kittiwakes, Puffins and other seabirds had a sequence of seven or eight disastrous breeding seasons. When commercial sandeel fishing in Shetland waters was banned in 1991, the breeding success of Arctic Terns in particular rocketed back to more normal levels, but the precise relationship between sandeel stocks of the right size and in the right place, fishing and terns is not at all easy to determine. The link *seems* obvious, but obvious conclusions are not always correct and there are clearly some very complicated factors at work. Even so, the catching of huge numbers of sandeels to feed to pigs or to squeeze into oil to fire power stations in Denmark does seem a somewhat obscene use of marine resources (or, put another way, of live fish).

Apart from fish, terns eat a variety of other food. Crustaceans are frequently on the menu. Shrimps, prawns, shore crabs and, in America, mole crabs, are taken regularly and in some studies it seems that (at least with shrimps) larger than average prey is selected. Insects are caught both on the ground and, more often, in the air, and their larvae are taken from water. Beetles, cockchafers, moths and sometimes butterflies, caddisflies, ants, grasshoppers, mayflies, and even dragonflies, are all snapped up, and the opportunism of the bird is illustrated by a list of occasional insect prey that even includes bees. Worms and leeches are picked from fresh water, small squids from the sea.

There are a number of studies which show the relative importance of these various prey items in particular circumstances. Common Terns collected and dissected in Norfolk (48 adults) contained, by total number rather than by size or weight, 25·5 per cent whiting, haddock, herring or sprats, 14·8 per cent sandeels, 14·2 per cent crustaceans, 15·4 per cent annelids, 10·2 per cent molluscs and 14·7 per cent insects, mostly cockchafers. Sandwich Terns there contained 66 per cent fish and 32·5 per cent marine worms, while Little Terns contained 1·9 per cent fish and a remarkable 96·9 per cent crustacea.

On the Farne Islands, records made by watching the food given to chicks revealed 44 per cent of the prey items as sandeels, 38 per cent herrings and sprats and 11 per cent whiting. In other studies the herring/sprat group outnumbered sandeels, and this generally seems to be the case as the breeding season progresses and the chicks get bigger. On the Ythan, sandeels and herrings were the main prey at high tide, but at low tide shrimps and blennies became the most important element of the diet. On the Ribble, however, sandeels were the high-tide choice, replaced at low tide by sprats.

In West Germany, one study revealed that 75 per cent of the food passed to chicks was fish, while at a colony in Maine, USA, the chicks were fed solely on herring. Of 116 terns killed and analysed at North American colonies, the stomach contents were 95·5 per cent fish, mostly freshwater minnows and sandeels. In the Volga delta, in southern Russia, food was again found to be mostly fish, and the prey species varied according to the time of year, but included bream, roach, rudd, carp, bleak and sticklebacks. In Finland, sticklebacks were preferred (or, more accurately, probably most readily available).

It may well be asked what effect all these fishing terns have on their prey, the fish and shrimps. In general, it is clear that predators are controlled by the numbers of their prey, rather than the other way around. This seems a commonsense conclusion, otherwise the predators would diminish the numbers of prey and consequently leave themselves with nothing to eat, and starve until the prey recovered. There is no suggestion, as a general rule, that this boom-and-bust economy operates. Instead, the predator is in some way regulated by the prey and has a population size to suit. But this view is also somewhat simplistic, and predators can, certainly, reduce the numbers of their prey for a time, in a small area.

N.P. Ashmole, writing of the regulation of numbers in tropical seabirds, thought that the birds had little significant effect on fish numbers overall, but that competition did occur locally because the limited amount of available food was indeed depleted by the birds. Several later writers have attempted to contradict this and say that food is not limited and not depleted by the feeding seabirds.

K.E.L. Simmons wrote that conspicuous plumage, such as the white of Common Terns, had a socially advantageous function and both the finder of a shoal of fish and subsequent arrivals attracted by the activity of an eyecatching white bird must benefit.

The idea is that co-operation by birds in a flock exploits the fish more efficiently. All such theorizing, of course, has to accept the view that evolution, or natural selection, must act towards creating the best, most efficient answer to problems such as catching fish and living an unstressed, fulfilled life.

If social feeding is to be more efficient, there must be some form of co-operation that makes it so. It assumes that the food is locally, temporarily at least, concentrated in greater numbers at certain spots than over the general region (such as small fish in dense shoals in an otherwise empty sea). It must also require that the amount of food found at such a 'hot spot', or patch, and the accessibility of the food to the birds, must not be reduced by the presence of the feeding flock.

David C. Duffy of the American Museum of Natural History studied the relationships between fishing Common Terns and their prey, butterfish, on Great Gull Island, New York. Duffy attempted to test the conflicting theories. He watched the feeding terns and measured the turnover of birds in feeding flocks and also the success rate of diving birds. He was also able to get a good indirect measure of the amount of food, which is rare.

The prey, butterfish, lives amongst the tentacles of jellyfish and seems to be immune to the poison in them. Duffy snorkelled and boated over the jellyfish and made sample counts and measurements of them and also of the associated butterfish. The topography and the tides meant that jellyfish were concentrated in certain small areas.

Anything from three to thirty fish were noted per jellyfish. The terns fed with little or no aggression between them and no territorial defence of feeding areas. Once they caught a fish, most terns left to take it directly to a nesting colony.

Duffy's observations fitted a pattern whereby the number of available fish limited the number of terns feeding at the food-rich patch where jellyfish were abundant. The turnover of terns feeding in the patch increased as jellyfish numbers increased. This seems to show that terns can catch food more easily, or more quickly, when there is more of it, a not unexpected conclusion perhaps.

The turnover of fishing terns was reduced when there were few birds, but also when numbers went beyond a certain high level. This was interpreted by Duffy to mean that, when there were few terns feeding, there was less food about and they had to spend more time hunting. When there were many more terns and food was more abundant, the success of fishing terns was reduced by disturbance from too many birds. If interference was simply causing greater turnover, then turnover should continue to increase with greater numbers. But terns spend much more time searching for prey than actually catching it and it seems better (that is more efficient) for a tern to spend a longer time in a crowded area, eventually getting a fish, than to leave altogether and have to find a new place with food available. Such a place might be a long way off and turn out to be just as crowded, anyway. So, very high tern numbers meant less success, but those that were there stuck at it longer.

The hunting success per dive was not altered by either jellyfish or bird numbers at the 'patch'. Duffy concluded that, when the turnover in terns was slower, the interval between dives was longer, but the birds dived only when they were pretty sure of success. Other observers, looking at Sandwich Terns, have also shown that diving rates change while success rates per dive do not. Again, it shows that the terns that are present when turnover is low have to try harder, or stay longer, but do so in order to ensure an eventual catch.

The jellyfish were constantly being swept into the fishing area by the tide. Butterfish, venturing out from their tentacles, were vulnerable to terns only for a matter of a few seconds at a time. Duffy thought that in such circumstances the chances of the terns reducing the numbers of butterfish substantially were very small. It seemed that the numbers of terns feeding at the patch depended entirely on the numbers of fish. The results appeared to Duffy to agree with Ashmole's theory in part: food may indeed be limited around seabird colonies, in that it is available only in relatively small areas, even if the overall numbers of prey species in the area are very large. But the predators did not appear to cause any long-term decline in the prey.

Duffy also studied the interactions between different species of terns feeding in his study area. Both Roseate and Common Terns often fed at an area 5·5 km from their colonies and showed no significant difference in the distance they were prepared to travel to find fish. The largest group of Roseate Terns was 34 (of a flock of 35 terns), only 2 per cent of the local population. The small group size of Roseate Terns compared with Common Terns was not, therefore, a function of population size. Common Terns fed in dense groups more often, with 63 per cent in dense groups, 23 per cent in 'medium' groups and fourteen per cent dispersed, while Roseates were feeding in a reversed pattern: 12 per cent in dense groups and 69 per cent dispersed.

Common Terns were more successful feeders than Roseates in dense groups, but less successful in smaller groups or when dispersed. So, flocking actually did increase the hunting success for Common Terns. Common Terns appeared to take fractionally larger prey than Roseates, but in most instances it was not significant. Commons also took more variety of fish than Roseates (averaging 15·8 types of prey per year, compared with 6·8 types) and were more successful at catching species of fish that were not locally very abundant.

Aggressive encounters were frequent in Duffy's flocks. Individual Common Terns were involved in some sort of disruptive activity less often than were Roseates feeding nearby. Dense flocks produced much more aggression among Roseates, perhaps fifteen times more frequent encounters than in dispersed groups. The aggression interfered with their foraging efficiency, so making a dispersed feeding strategy more effective for the Roseates.

The feeding terns formed what Duffy describes as inverted cones, with a few birds close to the surface and more terns, more widely spread, with increasing height. These were not flocks of terns cashing in on a superabundance of fish by catching them at will. The prey seemed to Duffy to be available only briefly in such situations, and then only under the point of the cone. Individual terns spent several minutes trying to get to the best position, at the foot of the cone, and to hold it

until a fish presented itself. The other members of the feeding flock hovered above, waiting for their chance.

If fish appeared, several birds plunged for them. The lowest birds had the best chance of success. Higher birds then often attempted to steal fish from the successful divers below. Roseate Terns seemed to be much more relegated to the periphery of the cone, rarely entering the fray in the centre. The cones frequently dispersed and re-formed in a matter of minutes, although some persisted for up to an hour.

In these cones, the dense feeding situations that Duffy described, the birds hovered, but elsewhere, where terns were dispersed, they were circling much more widely, gliding and sailing over greater distances, diving one or two at a time instead of joining in a mass hunt. The attrac-tion of a lively, excitable white flock seemed irresistible to some, but not to attract others, after all.

Food availability has a huge influence on the breeding success at a colony and, indeed, is probably one of the main factors that make tern colonies so erratic in their size and location from year to year. There will be more on this subject in a later chapter which deals with the breeding behaviour and success of Common Terns. Meanwhile, as I said at the beginning of this chapter, terns, as everyone knows, eat mostly fish.

Busy tern flocks make for spectacular birdwatching as they plunge for fish.

6

VOCABULARY

COMMON Terns make a lot of noise. They are among those birds that best conjure up images of the places where they live, where they seem to belong and help create the essential atmosphere and ambience of the environment. Common Terns are the essence of beach and estuary.

For most of us, there are individual bird species with a particular, very personal, connection with times and places fondly remembered, sometimes long gone. I cannot think of Oystercatchers without memories of western sea lochs in Scotland, magnificent fingers of glassy ocean that penetrate deep into the Argyll mountains, where the Oystercatchers' piping calls echo and re-echo every summer evening. Then, the thought of the sea lochs and the hills feeds more ingredients into the train of thought that takes me through so many interests and diversions of past years.

To think of the Shetlands instantly brings to mind the strange courtship calls of Red-throated Divers; while the lovely, subdued yodels of Long-tailed Ducks and the sensual croonings of Eiders takes me back to eastern Scottish firths. Terns obviously remind me of sea coasts, too, their calls especially associated with Norfolk beaches and sandy firths in Easter Ross. Common Terns, through their calls, have, like the Oystercatchers and the Eiders, the capacity to transport me far away from home and office to some remote shore where I really want to be.

When there are many of them together, and they are in an excitable frame of mind, Common Terns can be extremely vocal. They produce a variety of sharp, grating, screeching sounds, often with a squeaky quality. Their voices involve frequent use of 'e', 'i' and 'k' sounds: long and harsh, or short, staccato vowels and clipped, hard consonants. The general effect is distinctively tern-speak, but it requires close attention to work out just what is going on.

The Marples, in their book on terns, attempted a full and considered description of tern vocalizations. They developed a system of describing sounds in print, in order to give an idea of the phonetics – 'syllabication' they called it – the pitch, the speed and the quality of the sounds. The results are surprisingly effective, but are now, of course, overtaken somewhat by the use of sonagrams and other visual representations of sound and, more important, freely available sound recordings. Digital stereo recordings give extraordinary fidelity when reproduced from a compact disc through a decent set of speakers. The rush and squeal of a diving tern is enough to make you flinch.

As the Marples explained, some sounds produced by terns are very similar and need frequent repetition before the listener can really 'get the hang of them' and separate them in his own mind. They give an example of a call given by a Common Tern that is somewhere between 'chak' and 'chuk', while its mate close by is giving practically the same call, but more like something between 'chuk' and 'chik'. I know what they mean.

Too many bird calls are just a brief instant of sound that bears little or no resemblance to human speech or the written word. The volume of sound and the distance at which it is heard also affect the interpretation, and many a call can be 'blown away on the wind'. Often a call that, at moderate range, seems to have a hard, distinct consonant at beginning and end – such as 'keek' – becomes little more than the 'ee' sound at very close range, with an abrupt start and finish, just a closing of the throat without a proper enunciation of the 'k'.

Recordings, seemingly from close range, frequently 'remove' the consonants. There is also the reverse of this, as greater distance also softens the sound and the hard start and finish to a syllable are again lost, although the richer, deeper resonances and throaty notes disappear, too, leaving a tinny, thin effect (listen to singing Skylarks at close range and high up, far off in the sky, and you will see what I mean).

A sand dune with sparse marram is a typical site for a nesting Common Tern, which calls frequently to its incoming mate.

This Common Tern is calling to a bird overhead as it incubates its eggs.

But the bird book's attempt to write down calls needs more than just a jumble of vowel sounds. Even 'cuckoo' might properly be described as 'u-oo', but 'cuckoo' is a more practical solution to the problem.

With the Common Tern, so much depends on the understanding of qualifying words – harsh, rasping, gentle, screeching, clipped, nasal, and so on – that any attempt to write down the calls so that a visitor from another planet might understand them is almost bound to fail. Instead, it must be assumed that most readers will have heard something from a tern, or have access to a decent recording, so that the descriptions presented in this chapter will make a little more sense. I often think that field-guide notes on bird calls serve merely to remind readers of what they have already heard, and fail to convey much about the real quality of a call that is yet to be experienced.

Compared with the Arctic Tern, the Common Tern produces calls that are somewhat harsher, more rasping and lower in pitch. Otherwise the range of calls and the circumstances in which they are given are very much alike. According to *The Birds of the Western Palearctic*, upon which this account is largely based, the most distinctive calls of the Arctic Tern are a harsh 'kee-arr', given in alarm, with the emphasis on the second syllable, compared with the Common Tern's 'kee-yah', with the emphasis on the *first* syllable. The Arctic Tern also has a scolding 'kit-it-it-kaar', emphasizing the final syllable, and some 'whistled or squeaked notes', sounding like 'kee' and 'peet'. I suspect I've lost you already.

In the Marples' book, imaginative use of typesetting shows the rise and fall of these notes with rising and falling letters on the page, something I can recommend for anyone's handwritten field notes that attempt to transcribe a strange call. It works. Failing that, draw a line above the transcription of the call, bending it up and down above the appropriate letters with the pitch of the sound. That works well, too.

Harsh alarm calls are frequently given by Common Terns standing on the ground.

The Common Tern's alarm call is harsh, shrill and more or less prolonged, best written 'keee-arrr', 'ke-arr' or 'kee-yah', which can be given from the ground or in flight. The emphasis is often on the first syllable, as already mentioned, but can be on the second, and sometimes the whole call becomes practically monosyllabic, like 'keeerr'. It begins, at least, lower than an Arctic's comparable call.

This alarm call is used when another Common Tern approaches a feeding territory or favoured roost site, being repeated at increasing frequency if the trespasser continues to come closer. The alarm becomes a threat. The Marples felt that it was given in a less intense form if the object of alarm was one that was familiar and presented little genuine threat; then the call becomes longer and lazier. Normally, it is an explosive, emphatic sound, especially if there should be a threat to a nest with well-incubated eggs or small chicks.

A shorter, sharper version – 'kyar' – shows greater fear. It is often given just as a bird takes flight and has a remarkable effect on surrounding terns, instantly quietening them and making them pay attention to the impending threat.

Another call, described in *BWP* as an anger call, is a staccato, stuttering 'kek-kek-kek-k-k', particularly frequent from males that are fighting over territories. It is used during dives on other Common Terns and also against predators that threaten to penetrate the colony. It is hard to say 'ka' or 'ke' quickly enough to reproduce the right staccato, chattering effect, which is almost like a rattling of stones. (Close the doors, make sure no-one is about, and try it.) Some individuals, more than most, work themselves into a real frenzy, with 'ki' and 'kear' notes and the rattling chatter all used to great effect, enough to panic many predators and see them off the property, although the serious ones – such as egg-eating gulls and foxes – seem to carry on regardless.

Extreme anger and real aggression result in a long, tearing growl, 'kaaarrr', used in beak-to-beak confrontations on the ground and in close-contact aerial manoeuvres. If you approach a nest with chicks, the terns will dive at your head, using loud 'ki-kii-kikikiki' notes that develop into 'kakakakakaka' with a piercing, screaming 'kaarrrrr' as they swoop by your ear or strike home with their bills, and it is easy to believe that the sound is more of anger than of fright. The fright afflicts the unwary intruder, not the dashing, confident tern. If a tern itself is frightened – perhaps pursued too intently by a gull or a skua – the vocal response is a trembling, repeated squeal.

When a tern is returning to its nest, often as it carries a fish back to its mate or to feed to its young, it uses a call that evidently identifies it as friend, not foe. This is the advertising call: 'It's okay, dear, don't worry, it's just me, and I've got you a nice fat fish.' The sound is transcribed as 'keea', 'keeur' or 'kierr', and is extended to 'keeuri' or 'kee-eri' once the vicinity of the nest is reached. This triple-note rhythm is one that all tern-watchers soon become familiar with.

The calls begin as soon as the bird catches a fish, and are repeated all the way back to the nest. Once there, the sounds give the impression of considerable excitement and they have, as the Marples describe, a peculiarly wild effect. They said that, while holding a fish 'does not diminish the vigour of the call', it does 'interfere somewhat with the articulation, giving the "song" a short-tongued sound'.

Similar sounds are used in defence of the nest; and also outside the breeding season, when they seem to be contact notes which help to maintain a loose link within the flock. Flocks of terns newly arrived in winter quarters, and also out on the fishing grounds offshore, use these calls in a subdued way, with little or none of the excitement and passion so characteristic of the calls around the breeding colony.

When a male is carrying a fish over the territory, or he is simply flying around looking for a potential mate, he gives a more developed version of the advertising call, written as 'keeur keeuri keeri keeri keeri'. The first two notes descend, and the rest become increasingly high-pitched.

The 'kor-call', is a low, quick repetition of a short note – 'korkor-korkrrr' – given by the male as he passes a fish to his mate in the air. This may be linked with the earlier advertising call into a more complicated performance.

I like the Marples' descriptions of the terns' calls in aerial displays. In the 'fish-chase', both terns call quickly, but not loudly, one with a fish and the other chasing, or being chased. They thought that it was the bird that carried the fish that gave a 'kari' call (the 'kar' guttural and rough, the 'i' very short) while the other responded with a short 'ti--ti--ti'. But real 'sky courting' brings the splendid and more complicated performances – 'loud, passionate "Chutta-che-a" and variations', the 'che' lower than the start and finish of the call. Sometimes the 'che-a' becomes 'che-e', rising in a particularly excited sound,

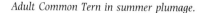

Adult Common Tern in summer plumage.

or the whole call becomes 'Chutterterde-e'. Such gobbledygook does convey something of the performance – if you read it with sufficient brio – but you must also imagine the effect of two birds calling together, one with passionate 'chuttachea's the other with little, quiet 'kwi' sounds in reply. And most likely there are several other pairs doing the same thing, not far away, so the whole sky is full of calls and responses, energy and passion. Tern calls are nothing if not emotive.

The 'kip-call' is a short, high note, well rendered 'kip' but with more or less of a squeaky quality that can make it sound like 'i', 'ki' or 'ik', one of those frustratingly brief little sounds that is neither one thing nor the other (a little like a wet finger rubbed hard for a centimetre or so against a pane of glass or a squeaky chalk on a board). It is a call of an excited tern, given in many contexts, most predictably from a tern that is just taking off from its territory. It is also a call of an excited, or maybe frustrated, fishing bird. A large shoal of fish giving easy fishing, or a tricky fish that requires several dives and repeated adjustments of height and angle, can stimulate these little, nervy sounds.

Similar calls are used by parent terns as signals to their chicks. Their meaning may simply depend on the situation at the time. If a chick is hiding, 'kik' can mean 'okay, come out now, it's safe'; but, if the chick is active, 'kik' can mean 'hide!' or 'keep still!'. It is rather like a toggle switch, the same thing producing opposite effects in successive operations. It may also simply answer a fledged juvenile that is flying around pestering its parents, begging for food.

The begging call is a hoarser version of the similar sound used by the Arctic Tern, but still shrill: 'ki-ki-ki' or 'kye-kye-kye'. Typically, this is used by a female begging for food from a male, but it can also be used by a male soliciting fish from a female or, perhaps in a temporary aberration, from a passing male.

A pair of Common Terns actively courting each other, on the ground, give soft, almost chuckling calls, sounding much like 'kruk-uk-k-k'. The same sound is heard from a bird in display flight suddenly gliding down, with its wings held in a deep 'V'. The same chuckling noises seem to be comforting, friendly calls that help relieve tension and break down the barriers to close approach that usually keep most individuals physically apart. Chuckles are used by a tern that arrives at the nest, ready to take its share of incubation. They also show that a parent is ready to brood small chicks and is gathering its little family together. The young, or a brooding adult, are treated to the same calls by a bird arriving with fish. They are simply notes of intimacy and familiarity, removing inhibitions and strengthening family ties.

Another call is termed the 'gurr-call', a growling 'kruu-krurr-krurr' or 'kerkerker', which both male and female produce when they are making a nest scrape in sand or shingle. It is a combination of this and the 'kruk-uk' sounds described above that gives a large colony a background noise, a low, rhythmic rumbling and bumbling sound that periodically rises to a more excitable utterance. There is a strange circumstance, of which more will be said in a later chapter, when the general hubbub of a colony rises to a fever pitch, then suddenly ceases and all the terns fly off out to sea. This is the remarkable 'dread', when some nameless fear grips the birds and they all react at once, although there is no sign of whatever it may be that is responsible.

Another Marples transcription is irresistible: a tern alighted and walked to the nest, calling 'tiu-tiu-tiu-grougrougrougrouchuchuchugrou tiu-tiu'. Its mate, unimpressed by this, said nothing. Unlike most other notes, in that it lacks any harsh element, a rather musical 'kleea' is sometimes uttered by a bird in solo display flight.

These are the calls of adult terns, mostly in or around the colony. There are also distinct sounds made by young birds. As soon as they are hatched, the chicks are vocal. Until they are eight or nine days old they give squeaky chirps and cheeps, feeble at first but soon becoming stronger. Once the feathers begin to grow, the cheeps are replaced by louder, rasping 'ki' notes, like coarser, higher-pitched versions of their parents' food-begging calls. These calls are used repeatedly even as late as the migration to Africa. At around 35–40 days old, the young accompany their parents on fishing forays, calling all the time, often answered by 'kip' notes from their parents.

These attempts to describe the calls of Common Terns nevertheless fail to convey the real spirit of the birds, among the most evocative of the lot when it comes to conjuring up an image of the ocean and windswept dunes. Their voices are wild, emphatic, ecstatic: singularly appropriate for birds of their salty, stormy, wide-skied realm.

7

SOCIAL BEHAVIOUR

WHEREVER and whenever you see a Common Tern, it is, so long as it is alive and well, likely to be responding to some sort of stimulus. This may be an internal one, perhaps depending on some hormonal state that affects the way the bird behaves. Or it may be an external one, whether it be from another Common Tern, or a predator, or the sight of potential prey, or simply some other factor such as a fast-rising tide that is about to push it off the rock on which it is resting.

Behaviour is a complicated and broad subject. 'Everyday' behaviour is not what is usually meant by birdwatchers who use the term, any more than we talk of people 'behaving' when they are simply doing ordinary things, such as sitting in front of the television or scratching their heads. In human terms, we concentrate, instead, on particular aspects of behaviour, good or bad, or out of the ordinary.

For birds, we do not refer to an overall impression or character, such as 'well behaved', when talking of behaviour, but to particular acts, most of which are more or less stereotyped and liable to be repeated. We may refer more generally to 'breeding behaviour' or some similar vague umbrella term, but as a rule we tend to mean a more identifiable action. We are not talking of twitches, or generosity, or a tendency to steal from others (the sort of human behaviour that gets noticed), but of specific actions that indicate a particular state inside the bird, or a particular reaction to some external pressure.

In general, the actions are characteristic of the species as a whole, not so much individual idiosyncrasies. Otherwise, they would not work. A meaningful posture adopted by one individual tern is repeated more or less exactly by hundreds and thousands of others of the same species and communicates the same message. If not, it would not be meaningful.

This similarity of behaviour, and, indeed, appearance, food and other factors, is one of the essential planks of bird biology and even ordinary birdwatching, allowing everything from serious scientific study to simple identification. Without the basic homogeneity of a species, the species itself should not be maintained and we would be faced with birds of random colour, pattern and lifestyle with no chance of putting the elements of their lives into any kind of order or categories at all. Actually, because their breeding systems would not work, such a random collection of individual birds could not exist.

It is an obvious point, but one often not appreciated by the non-birdwatcher, who has never really thought of what it is that keeps different species of birds separate. I well remember, while watching a high-tide roost of waders, being asked why it was that the black birds (Oystercatchers) did not mingle with the white ones (gulls). Behind the question was the muddled idea that a bird is a bird (as if 'bird' was the species, like 'dog' or 'cat') and that, given a bit of interbreeding over a few years, all these birds flocking together at high tide would become intermediate grey ones (mongrels).

This Common Tern with raised wings and upstretched head calls to another tern flying overhead.

In fact, the relative constancy of behaviour, calls and so on within a species is a remarkable thing. So many thousands are so stereotyped as if they are clones of the original, in a superficial view, although there is variety and change going on all the time (the stuff of evolution). One Common Tern, let us say, gives a 'keeyah' or 'kip' call that is duplicated with amazing precision (to the human ear) by every other Common Tern. And the threat posture of one territorial male is the same as the threat posture of any other territorial male. It has to be, or other terns would not 'realize' that they were being threatened and react accordingly. But note the inverted commas: realization is not quite the conscious thing we might expect in human terms.

Bryan Nelson, in his book *Seabirds: their biology and ecology*, contends that seabirds should not be considered to understand the purpose of their behaviour, in terms of understanding what it is they are trying to achieve by performing special actions or giving particular calls. They simply go through the motions that are programmed into them genetically. Once the response is 'correct', they then 'know' that the purpose has been achieved and move on to the next part of the programme.

In other words, a Common Tern does not see a rival, feel angry and decide: 'I know what I'll do, I'll droop my wings, lean forward to show off my black cap and scream at him – that should see him off'. Instead, the sight of a rival, or a trespasser, automatically triggers off a response which, because the rival will also be programmed to respond, will do the job required. It is a fascinating thought that all this complex and often attractive (to us) behaviour is simply a set of reactions that bear no more relation to logical thought than, say, our pulling a hand away from a hot iron or flinching and blinking an eye to keep out a stray kamikaze midge. The increased realization that humans have many unconscious actions and responses is illustrated by the increase in popular, amateur study of 'body language'.

Nevertheless, it is always interesting to speculate just what goes on inside a Common Tern's head. One of us, listening to a group of people talking loudly and quickly in a foreign tongue, might describe the 'call' as an irregular babble. Detecting the nuances of tone and emphasis, which endow human speech with such a complicated set of meanings and implications, is not easy (even with someone speaking the same language in a different dialect). Shrink yourself down to tern size, with the speed of reaction and metabolism of a bird, and the shades of meaning in calls, postures and other aspects of behaviour might be much more individual than we can imagine. There are examples, for instance, of birds recognizing the calls of mate or chick, or even the individual smell of an occupied burrow, in what to us seems like a multitude of identical circumstances.

The Flock

Much Common Tern behaviour is concerned with communicating with other Common Terns, giving them messages and also expecting some sort of response in return. The species is fundamentally a social one, and there needs to be a good deal of organization going on within flocks and breeding groups. What goes on within a flock of Common Terns to keep the social group orderly and working well together? Why flock in the first place?

There are several likely benefits. The improved performance of a feeding flock compared with individual birds in some circumstances has already been discussed in Chapter Five. In one study in the USA, 63 per cent of Common Terns watched were feeding in dense flocks, 23 per cent in small groups and the rest were dispersed. Feeding flocks are most frequently small, up to around ten birds, but can be as big as two hundred. Along coasts of fairly uniform appearance, such as the long shingle banks of north Norfolk, quite where a flock ends is not always obvious, but it depends partly on what you call a flock. Often the terns are loosely dispersed, but each well within sight of the next, all along the beach until a particularly dense shoal of fish concentrates some of them in one spot.

Where food is abundant, such as a dense shoal of small fish easily visible at the surface, there is no need for a tern to defend its own feeding territory, because there is more than enough to go around. It is better for all the terns if they can spot a colleague fishing successfully, fly over to join him and dive in. This is where the sparkling white plumage comes in so useful. Rather than scores of terns laboriously searching for individual fish, they come together in a flock where the fish are most concentrated. It is, then, every tern for itself. In summer, feeding groups may mix with Arctic, Sandwich and Little Terns, but African winter flocks may be a much more varied lot, with Black, Royal, Lesser Crested, Roseate and Caspian joining in, too. The flock is visibly excited, noisy and hyperactive.

This is something that applies commonly to many bird species. Finches illustrate the argument well. In summer, Chaffinches looking for caterpillars need to defend a territory, because the caterpillars are dispersed and require searching out one by one. Linnets, on the other hand, are looking for seeds. Where there are seeds, there are more than enough to go round for several pairs; elsewhere there are none at all. So while Chaffinches nest pair by pair in well-defined territories, feeding apart, Linnets nest in small groups and benefit by being able to gather together whenever one finds a good source of food. Being close together at night means that the Linnets that have not had much luck during the day can the next morning follow those that found an abundance of food. Chaffinches remain dispersed; Linnets become clumped.

With the tern and its fish, the strategy changes from hour to hour. If the fish are dispersed, the tern feeds alone like a Chaffinch. If a big shoal appears for a while, the terns gather like hungry Linnets. The more flexible approach is ideally tailored to suit the changing circumstances.

Flocks have other benefits. According to studies at an estuary, a wader feeding on its own is three times more likely to be caught by a Merlin than is a wader in a flock. A similar protection against predation probably applies to individual terns within a flock, whether it be fishing, loafing or roosting. A tern (or the wader) with its head down, looking for food, is less likely to notice a predator coming up from behind, but it has to take the risk because it must eat. If it is with a score or two of other birds of its kind, the chances are that not all will be preoccupied with food at any one time, and one of them will spot the approaching falcon, give the alarm and offer all of them a sporting chance to escape.

There is perhaps the comforting thought, too (not conscious, of course), that if a Peregrine comes along it is best to be in a flock because the

The appearance of this Merlin is panicking all the birds at this estuary, although the Peregrine is usually more of a threat to the terns.

chances are it will catch one of the others. If it finds you alone, it has no option and you become the next meal. The best place to hide a needle is not in a haystack, but in a heap of other needles.

A flock of terns, like a flock of Oystercatchers, probably also has a confusing effect on an attacking Merlin or Peregrine. The sudden flurry of wings must distract the hunter and make it difficult for it to concentrate on one individual. In the confusion of a flushed flock, the strike is missed and the terns escape.

A flock, too, has a much better chance of turning on a predator to drive it away. A single bird would risk too much to take on a deadly foe, but a flock might do the trick. This is probably a major reason for Common Terns nesting in colonies.

Whether flying or standing, Common Terns keep their individual minimum distances intact. A lean forward and a sharp jab of the bill both maintains the space and dictates the distance that can be defended. It may be reduced, though, when terns squeeze on to a suitable perch, such as a buoy on a reservoir, or the side of a moored boat. A dozen or two, resting on migration, may then shuffle together, but bickering and short flights often break out to upset the temporary harmony.

On migration, Common Terns travel mostly in small groups, perhaps of ten or a dozen. In the autumn there may be families travelling together, but flocks composed solely of juveniles can also be encountered. In winter, flocks are frequently still of mixed ages, and family parties probably persist for some months. In spring, flocks travelling north to the breeding colonies include some pairs already established. When they reach the region of the breeding colony, terns that are already paired can be picked out because they stand and roost closer together than the others and sporadic bursts of courtship behaviour give them away.

Night is a dangerous time for terns and they usually roost in flocks. They tend to prefer open ground where they can be well away from cover or broken ground, so big beaches, mudflats, large saltpans and so on are ideal. Offshore rocks, piers and other man-made features surrounded by water are also safe roosts. Sometimes, at least on migration, flocks rest on the sea. In the Gulf of Guinea, flocks have been seen feeding from first light until dark 600 km from the coast, and presumably they must remain airborne all night or roost on the water.

The colony

Terns in general have a number of characteristics in common. Most of the sea terns, at least, like our subject, the Common Tern, nest in colonies. This instantly injects a conflict of interest: the need to nest close together, contrasted with the desire to stay apart. There is the clash of a social breeding pattern with the territoriality of individual pairs. Indeed, before even this stage, while pairs have yet to be formed, there is the problem of individual distance to be overcome by birds that have to make physical contact.

Although wanting to defend a territory from other, trespassing terns, the Common Tern does not really want to spend half its life fighting and fussing when it has more important things to be getting on with (such as eating, and feeding the chicks). Nor does it wish to risk real damage in a fight. To win a dispute at the expense of a broken wing is total defeat. Other behavioural features have developed to preclude such damage, to help a tern assert its dominance over another without necessarily coming to bone-breaking blows. The whole area of aggression and appeasement is a rich field for the student of bird behaviour.

Compared with most gulls, terns are rather less strongly territorial. This seems to be connected with the fact that they hold smaller territories and have less strongly developed actions to defend a larger, more vulnerable area. Also, while gulls quite often kill other gulls' chicks if they stray from one nest site to another, terns rarely do so and the sharply defined and fiercely defended territory so necessary to the gulls is less essential to terns.

Also in comparison with gulls, terns tend to be much more aerial in their display and aggressive encounters, less likely to scrap among themselves, or show off to others, on the ground. The Common Tern has long, aerial pursuit flights in which males fly up to great heights, but larger tern species, such as the Caspian, do not have these. The Common and Arctic (medium-sized) group is among the most aerial of all.

There are odd descriptions of terns' behaviour towards a dead or injured member of the colony. If there is an injured Common Tern trying to fly or run, making a noise and easily detected, the rest of the tern flock may gather overhead, calling noisily. There is little comfort in this for the injured tern: indeed, it may be attacked by its neighbours, even killed. But, if there is a dead, injured or sick tern that simply squats motionless and silent near the colony, the others hover above it, silently.

Immature birds visiting a colony for the first time, but not breeding, probably learn by observing the social behaviour of the colony that this is the best place to nest, that the colony offers the best opportunities for future success.

Most colonies are located on areas of uniform ground, but some are broken and feature a central group on a marsh with, for example, a sub-group alongside on a sandy ridge. In the 1974 survey of coastal colonies in Britain and Ireland, the average size was 263 pairs. In Virginia, USA, the average was 95, while in New Jersey colony size varied from one to 554 pairs in the mid-1970s. Only rarely do colonies reach more than 1500–2000, although one exceptional site in the Netherlands had a magnificent colony of up to 25,000 pairs for many years. Inland colonies are smaller, on average, and rather more dispersed than the tightly knit groups on the coast.

On arrival in spring, the first birds back do not necessarily even visit the colony. The Marples reckoned that the early arrivals stayed out at sea, not even coming ashore at first, followed by a period of short visits to the colony but no long stays. Later arrivals, the Marples said, immediately occupied the shore close to the colony and then entered the nesting area (although some would later move on). Their visits to the ternery were detected both by visual observation and the presence, or absence, of tracks in the sand.

One year at Blakeney was described. The terns had arrived in numbers and were flying over the ternery by 26 April. On 28 April, terns roosted near the ternery for the first time. On 29 April, some alighted within the ternery itself. On 1 May, for the first time, there were 'myriads of footprints in the sand on the breeding grounds showing walking, standing, and displaying-tracks and the first "false" nests, indicating that, in the early dawn, the breeding ground had been invaded. As on the last few days, the ternery has been deserted during the day: none have alighted there and few have flown over it.' Much the same

Common, Arctic and Roseate Tern plumages.

Roseate Tern
(breeding)

Arctic Tern
(breeding)

Common Tern
(black-billed form)

Roseate Tern
(late summer)

Common Tern
(breeding)

Common Tern
(non-breeding)

Common Tern
(juv.)

Norman Arlott.

happened on 2 and 3 May; on 4 May, the terns had evidently roosted overnight in the colony. By 18 May the terns all seemed to be paired, and on 19 May the first egg was laid.

There is a lot of co-operative action to be seen in a tern colony. If a bird sees danger approaching (a fox, a human, or a Peregrine perhaps), it gives a loud 'kyar' call, sometimes with raised wings (which no doubt enhance its ability to gain attention). Then it flies up with rapid, deep wingbeats. This is the alarm to the rest of the colony, and the other birds are quick to react. They stop calling (something which is often dramatic to people watching and listening) and look about. If they decide to fly, they fly up and keep quiet, until the flock has gathered itself in the air above the colony.

'Dreads' are strange features of the colony's behaviour. Some or all of the terns quite suddenly, with no obvious warning, get up and fly low and silently to the sea in a dense flock. It is a peculiar act which grabs the attention of any watcher because it is such an abrupt change from the noisy business of colony life. After some minutes, individual birds begin to call and drift back again to their appointed places.

These dreads are most common in dense colonies, and the excited social stimulus of a close-packed, large group of nesting or courting birds seems to be partly responsible for the actions, although probably a response to some predator may also be involved.

Ground-nesting birds such as terns are inevitably vulnerable to predators, which can effectively just walk or fly in and take their pick unless the terns' defences are such that its intentions can be resisted. Birds that nest in colonies, like terns and Black-headed and Lesser Black-backed Gulls, show a preference for nesting where the pairs are densest. Nests in the dense centre of a colony are more successful than those on the edge, where the eggs and chicks are naturally more vulnerable. An aerial predator finds more resistance in a dense part of the colony than at the edge, and a ground predator comes across the outer nests first, without causing such a fuss among the occupants.

The habitat selected also helps to deter predators. Open, bare sand or shingle provides little or no cover for a prowling predator. On the North Sea coast and Sweden, it has been shown that Common Tern colonies with shrubs and trees are more likely to be preyed on than open ones, because the predators can secrete themselves in the vegetation and do much more damage before they are discovered. Mink are unable to attack a colony in the open, at least in daylight, because of the aerial bombardment from the terns, but they can effectively prey on colonies which they can approach under cover. In Finland, crows can attack Common Tern colonies with great effect if there are trees nearby, but not if they are in the open.

To work well, the colony must be properly synchronized. The benefits of large numbers of birds nesting close together in space can be enjoyed only if they also nest closely in time.

The behaviour of individual birds in a colony is likely to influence the behaviour of others nearby. Displays become contagious, and there is therefore an increased tendency for the whole cycle to peak at one time throughout a colony. There are periods (as in bad weather) when displays are reduced in frequency, and a consequent upsurge among a number of pairs, when conditions become favourable again, can be misinterpreted as a bout of displays synchronized for some other reason. Nevertheless, in general it has been shown that Common Terns displaying and mating do tend to stimulate other pairs nearby to do the same. By bringing the whole colony (or perhaps an identifiable sub-colony within it) to the boil at once, social stimulation ensures that all the terns will be ready to defend the colony, as a community, when defence is most needed. The colony produces the most efficient environment for breeding terns; the breeding terns produce the most effective behaviour to consolidate the colony.

8

THE TERRITORY

THE territory dealt with here is the small area of defended ground immediately around the nest. Common Terns may also defend temporary fishing territories, but basically the only piece of territory to which they claim exclusive rights is the nest site itself.

Several studies have illustrated the average distance between nests on uniform ground. In one colony of 55 pairs in Virginia, the nests were separated by 160 cm, while a study in the former USSR showed the mean distance to be 350 cm, with a minimum of 50 cm. Other nests have been found as little as 43 cm apart.

The defended area around the nest is small and roughly circular (related to the reach of the bird, with the defensive weapon – the bill – at one end). Separate studies have shown 2–3 m² to be the average size of this core territory, but it can be smaller and also more irregular in shape on uneven ground. It is also clear that the boundary of the defended area is not fixed throughout the season and early-season sparring can squeeze less aggressive pairs at the expense of more dominant, expansive neighbours.

This tiny territory is the focal point for the central features of the breeding cycle, from pair-formation to nesting and the feeding of the chick until it is able to fly. It becomes the focus of the tern's life for several weeks, and not surprisingly the attachment to it is sufficiently strong to outlast the immediate needs of the short nesting season. If an adult tern breeds successfully and survives until the following spring, it may well return to precisely the same spot to defend its territory again. One pair was found to occupy the same territory for seventeen years, until one of the two died.

Arctic terns have much the same commitment to a nest site, returning again and again after journeys to the Antarctic and back, to reoccupy the same little group of sub-Arctic rocks or favoured patch of sand. It is a minor miracle repeated millions of times over, by many species of bird. The Swallow in the garden shed is likely to be the very same one as a year ago. The Chiffchaff singing from the poplar tree is, most likely, the same Chiffchaff as the one that sang there twelve months before. Also, birds that arrive in Britain in winter are returning to familiar winter beats of previous years: gulls, geese, swans and many more all repeat the pattern.

Sandwich Terns, by comparison, have less fidelity than Commons to a traditional nest site. They arrive at a colony and settle down quickly, lay eggs and get the job over and done with as quickly as possible. If they are disturbed at the egg-laying stage, they have no attachment to the site and simply desert. This may help prevent the colony being decimated by predators later on, after much more effort has been expended, and gives the Sandwich Tern that frustrating characteristic, for conservationists, of erratic, unpredictable occupancy of breeding sites. Buy a Sandwich Tern colony and make it into a nature reserve and they will probably repay you by nesting somewhere else the following year.

In one study, 90 per cent of the experienced breeding Common Terns returned to the same territory they had fought for and defended the year before. This is helped by the fact that these older birds, ones that have bred before, return to the colony somewhat earlier than young, first-time breeders, and so they get back to stake their claim without too much trouble from intruders. It is up to the later birds to work harder to get a foot in at the door of the colony. They can do so by nesting at the edge, or by finding bereaved birds on territories, whose mates have failed to return. Younger terns, however, although they tend to return to breed in the area where they were reared, are much more likely to move from one colony to another for a year or two before settling down into an established pattern.

Like Gannets, immature terns, attending the colony but not yet breeding, gather together on the colony fringe in 'clubs'. These may be joined by breeders that are 'off duty' taking a nap while the mate incubates the eggs. The club birds often gather below high-water mark and move with the tides. It is probable that they are getting a feel for

Display postures include the 'ground bent posture' adopted in territorial disputes.

colony life, some useful experience that will stand them in good stead in later years when they need to be properly synchronized and ready to act in concert with their neighbours. They are also probably stimulated by the social behaviour of the colony and become imprinted, in a sense, with the precise location of the successful site, so they will return the following year.

Competition for nest sites is intense, especially in large colonies or those with restricted areas of suitable ground so that space is a limiting factor, as on a small island or an artificial raft. Threats and actual fighting become more obvious then than in small, loosely dispersed colonies. Fighting and aggressive displays are also most frequent at the beginning of the season, before life in the colony has settled down to a more routine pattern.

If a male is on his territory – the couple of square metres around the nest – he will challenge any intruder, male or female. A female, however, is less likely to do so. If the intruder is a male with a fish in his beak, the female may even welcome his advances. If the pair is present together and an intruder appears, the male takes the initiative and acts to repulse the stranger; the female may help, but not for long.

A territory-holder ideally wants to repel intruders quickly and with minimum effort, most of all without risk of physical damage to himself. Here we have the pre-programmed actions and reactions coming into play. It is a general rule with all birds that the territory-holder is in the right and dominates the intruder. If that same intruder retreats to his territory, and the previous dominant bird trespasses, the tables are turned. The first intruder now becomes able to resist and repel the other bird. It is the strength given by possession of the territory that counts more than physical superiority. There is no thought process behind all this threat and submission. No tern thinks: 'He's much smaller than me, I can take him', or: 'He's much bigger than me, I'd best get out of here and let him have what he wants'. Instead, it is a predetermined set of actions and reactions, to the effect that: 'This bit is mine – get off' nearly always wins. It is less might is right, more right is might.

The territory-holder warns a trespasser approaching on foot by giving the alarm or advertising calls: 'keee-arrrr' or 'keeurr'. If the intruder keeps coming, the calls are repeated more rapidly and the defender raises his wings to enhance the effect. All the time the two will face each other in a special posture, called the 'ground bent posture' an intimidating pose involving a tilt forward of the head (emphasizing the black cap), a ruffling of the neck feathers (presumably to increase apparent size and strength), a raised tail and drooped inner wings, with the carpal joints (or 'wrists') pushed out from the sides. As the two approach closer, the posture is intensified. The head is bent forward even more, so that the bill points vertically down and almost touches the ground, the wings are pushed even wider (although the tips are still together under the tail), and the tail raised higher still.

This should do the trick. Here is the warning: 'I am on my territory, please keep off'; and the automatic reaction ought to be to back off. But some intruders take the threat a little further. The defender stops calling (a further warning that worse is to follow). Then, he will dart forward and grasp the other by the bill. Each bird tries to grasp the other and they may interlock bills, or one may succeed in holding the other by the head. This is not, apparently, an attempt to push the other bird away, but in fact seems to be a strenuous effort to pull it closer, to get more grip, perhaps to get a chance to strike a telling downward blow. The rightful owner of the territory often gives anger calls, loud, sharp 'kek-kek-kek-kek' notes. With such long, sharp bills, one obvious danger is that of being blinded as the open bill of one combatant grips the face of the other.

The ground bent posture is used by both trespasser and territory-holder in territorial disputes. Eventually the intruder will adopt the ground erect posture in defeat

The intruder now usually admits defeat and adopts a special appeasement posture, the 'erect posture'. His tail is lifted, his wings drooped, but the bill is raised upwards and pointed at the sky. Superficially it looks a triumphant pose, but it is the opposite. It seems to be a deliberate exposure of the throat, a vulnerable area, almost an invitation to stab and finish the fight. Of course, the victor refrains and simply sidles back to the centre of his circle.

When a pair is on the territory and another pair approaches too closely, the ritual is even more stereotyped. The defending terns bow repeatedly at the others, and the impression is strengthened by the fact that their bows are perfectly synchronized. The bow downwards is actually the 'bent posture' described above, while the upward part of the movement is a sudden switch to the 'erect posture' adopted by a defeated trespasser. All the time, the pair may well be calling repeatedly with 'keeurr' or 'kieerr' notes, the so-called advertising calls. The overall effect is sufficient to deter the other pair and the confrontation is usually soon over. To our eyes, the synchronization of movement adds not more impact, or severity of threat, simply more beauty to the moves. It is rather like watching a pair of ice-skaters spinning together, instead of one; somehow, the sum is greater than the two parts.

The airspace above the colony is also crucially important in the way the communal life of the terns is ordered. The centre of activity is again the small piece of territory on the ground. If the owner is away fishing when a trespasser appears, unchallenged, it reacts strongly and angrily on its return. The new arrival veers upwards and then swoops down, calling 'kek-kek-kek', to jab the unwanted visitor with its bill. The visitor is quickly overwhelmed and driven off by this painful lesson in where the rightful ownership belongs.

Birds meeting in the air, as inevitably happens with great regularity when neighbouring terns move in and out of their nest territories in the middle of a busy colony, simply fight. This generally becomes little more than a brief, angry, ill-tempered chase. But there may be an interesting development, one highly characteristic of Common Terns. This has been termed the 'upward flutter' flight.

Usually one bird flies just a little above the other, and the two slowly spiral with fast wingbeats reminiscent of the fishing hover. As they spin, so they rise vertically upwards. The Marples described this, emphasizing the rapidity of the wingbeats combined with the slowness of the ascent, as the birds rise up, in an almost upright position, with their tails widely spread. Now and then a spiralling duo will carry on rising until they are practically out of sight, before separating and drifting apart, although still flying with wingbeats of exaggerated speed.

During the ascent, one or both terns may call with sharp, staccato notes, and jab at the other with its bill, giving the impression that these flights are basically encounters of a hostile nature. Sometimes the rising flight breaks down quickly, or one bird dives at the other and drives it to the ground, only for another, longer 'upward flutter' to take place immediately afterwards. In their book on sea terns, the Marples gave one instance in which two Common Terns performed the upward flutter, swooped down and repeated the flutter no fewer than 27 times in succession.

This upward, spiralling, fluttering interaction is usually above a nesting territory, but the same pattern is followed during disputes over defended feeding territories, some way from the actual colony itself.

The actions used to defend a territory are frequently carried out by a pair in concert; but the interactions between the male and female are a different matter, courtship rather than territorial defence.

9

THE PAIR

ERNS, in general, keep at least a little apart, preserving their private, individual space (as we humans do). But to breed and successfully rear young, two must become intimate partners, willing to get close, touch, and pass food from bill to bill. Not only do they need to make contact, but, as with humans, regular contact maintains the bond between the pair and reinforces the trust between them.

Whether the 'trust' is conscious or not, it must be there because each individual is about to invest a great deal of its life and energy into an attempt to reproduce. To do so, it must have the full co-operation of another bird, and this must be one that can be relied upon to do its bit. If it is a female, it must be able to lay eggs and also willing to sit on them until they hatch. If it is a male, the female has to rely on him to feed her and later to feed the chicks, and not wander off on some business of his own when he is most needed.

To break down the resistance to physical contact, in order to achieve this happy state of partnership, requires some form of 'courtship display', special behaviour evolved to create acceptance of each bird by the other. Courtship display makes particular use of the more striking features of a Common Tern's appearance, particularly around the head, with that neat black cap and long red bill.

Any decent Common Tern will try to do the best it can by its offspring. This makes sense because it is attempting to continue the line of its own genes. It includes finding the best partner as the other parent. So, there has to be a way in which one tern can assess the suitability of another to be the father, or mother, of its young, so it can select the best mate. Behaviour again comes to the rescue. Special elements of a Common

An aerial equivalent of the 'bent posture' is sometimes employed by the male during courtship flight.

Tern's behaviour give clues to other Common Terns as to its ability to rear good, strong chicks and catch enough fish to feed them.

Pair-formation involves both aerial and ground displays at the colony. It should be remembered, however, that some pairs arrive at a colony in spring already paired up, and their behaviour is not so much a courtship from scratch as a reinforcement of established bonds.

Some courtship behaviour may be seen early in spring among groups of birds still on the last stages of their migration. Are these individuals that are pairing again, with the same partners, for another year? Have they been together all winter, or do they recognize each other now? It cannot be that they both return to the same nest and meet by accident, because they are already courting before they reach the colony.

Aerial courtship

There are three elements in aerial courtship, which is a major part of the early-season behaviour. These are termed 'high flight', 'low flight' and the 'pass ceremony'. The pass is the final phase of both of the other two.

High flight is the commonly seen piece of behaviour early in the season, when the pair is still very much uncertain and unconfirmed. The flight may begin after an 'upward flutter' when two neighbouring males rise in a spiral from their territories and then break apart, but it may also begin immediately after one of the strange 'dreads' that suddenly empties a colony of its birds in a silent rush to the sea.

The two birds circle together, with rapid wingbeats, rising to some 200 m. They are not necessarily so close together as in the hostile upward flutter. In fact, the two can be 50 m apart. As they rise, they keep apart, on diametrically opposite sides of the circumference of the imaginary circle that they describe in the air. The male most often carries a fish, but the female apparently never does so. It is the male that 'leads', while the female follows him on his spiral path.

The male, ahead, sometimes calls a sharp 'kip' note. Once the pair has reached a certain height, the following female catches up and flies just above or to one side of the male – this is the pass ceremony. In the descriptions earlier of aggressive encounters on the ground, mention was made of the 'erect posture' and the 'bent posture'. At the moment of the pass, the aerial versions of these are used. The female, flying past the male, uses the 'erect' posture, but in flight it is a 'straight' posture with head and bill outstretched, horizontally, but tilted away from the male, while the wings are curiously arched. The male may adopt the 'bent' pose, with his wings raised attractively in a 'V', and his head tilted downwards.

The female may call, giving the begging call ('ki-ki-ki'), instead of using the erect posture. The male may produce three distinct sounds. As the female catches him up, he may call 'keeurr'; then as she passes he calls 'kor kor korkrr', and sometimes he rounds off the procedure with the soft, chuckling notes of the 'kruk call'. The combination of raised wings, drooped head and this sequence of calls often draws attention to the pass, even if the initial upwards, circling rise has gone unnoticed in the general hubbub.

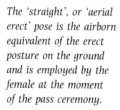

The 'straight', or 'aerial erect' pose is the airborn equivalent of the erect posture on the ground and is employed by the female at the moment of the pass ceremony.

It is worth picking up this performance, because now the female, in the lead, sways from side to side, sideslipping dramatically, and dives down very fast. During the glide, if there is sufficient height, the pass is performed again and again. Each time, the birds repeat their particular postures, in an increasingly intense manner. At the bottom of the glide, the two flatten out, swoop up and perhaps repeat the whole performance again, or they may simply drift apart and move off.

The high flight is such an important part of the tern's repertoire that it may perform it, so far as it can, on its own. On the other hand, several neighbouring terns may be caught up in the excitement and join in the fun.

The Marples describe beautiful forms of the downward glide with synchronized sideslips. They suggest holding out both hands, each with fingers widespread, one a little above the other; now sway them from side to side, tilting both one way then the other to keep them parallel and the space between them constant. This gives an impression of the appearance of the terns in this performance. At other times, the birds slip in opposite directions, just avoiding collision. The Marples clearly loved their terns: 'The longest "glide" we have timed was one hundred and sixty seconds without a break, performed by two sunlit, silver birds against an intense blue sky, a lovely sight.' So it is.

Again they write: 'Usually the "glide" seems slow and is certainly leisurely, but at times a sudden excitement overtakes the birds and they drop in the "downward rush". At an immense pace, without any wing flap, they fall from a height, "side slipping" in unison right and left until they reach the ground. Or they will "TUMBLE" with great speed, turning as they fall till the plane of their wings is vertical, first one wing being uppermost, then the other. The delirium may die down before they reach the ground, in which case they will resume their flight on a lower level.'

These descriptions particularly emphasize the rhythmic, sinuous side-to-side slips and tilts which give these flights such an air of excitement. As in the bowing by a pair on the ground, the synchrony of two birds in close proximity adds to the effect. The terns manage to combine their customary grace and lightness with a pace, determination and vigour the equal of many more powerful fliers.

The low flight is a variation initiated by a male, sometimes an unpaired one, but also by a male already firmly bonded to a female. He starts flying with his wings held up in a high 'V', using shallow, slow wingbeats and calling 'kieerr'. He may carry a fish. If he does so, he might attract another male, or a female may fly up with him. If he has no fish, other males ignore him and only a female will show interest. Whichever, the first male adopts the 'bent posture', wings up and head tilted down, which precipitates the pass ceremony.

If the male has a fish, the whole episode may develop into a full-blown high flight, complete with dives and several more passes. There are several possibilities, however. A pair may fly down to the ground, to continue courtship behaviour there, or the two may split up leaving the first male to go on to a high flight on his own.

'It appears rather that the fish is a symbol, rather than a comestible. One seems to be watching a swain offering a love gift, then snatching it away, being then chased by the lady, who presently tires of the game, or, piqued, flies away, in her turn to be followed by the repentant lover with his present.' *Sea Terns* makes rather more evocative reading, if less precise and objective, than *The Birds of the Western Palearctic*.

Ground courtship

On the ground, the courting terns look a little less graceful and fluent, their short legs inhibiting rapid and easy movement on foot. Early courtship behaviour simply exaggerates this, by consisting of odd, shuffling movements and incomplete posturing, as if a warming-up period is needed before the birds can really get into the swing of it all.

The low-flight encounters, however, gradually succeed in males enticing females to the ground more often and more readily. Then ground courtship begins in earnest. Usually it is in a territory already held by the soliciting male, but it can take place away from a territory.

I.C.T. Nisbet, who has studied Common Terns extensively in the USA, has worked out very many relationships of marked birds, and his observations show that courtship displays may involve birds of all sorts: well-established, faithful pairs; neighbours; birds of the same sex; old, experienced breeding birds displaying with young, new ones not yet paired; and so on. The tern colony is a complicated, difficult place to get to grips with.

A male on the ground with a female may or may not carry a fish. In either case, he adopts the bent posture, his neck arched and head bent down, wings pushed out from the body at the wrists, tail up. He usually faces a little to one side of the female and may even turn his head and bill away a little. If he is really meaning business, he tilts his whole body away, so much so that one wing is often touching the ground.

In this distinctive, strained pose, he walks in a circle around the object of his attentions. This is called the 'parade'. It is a peculiar walk, with short, quick steps, his neck craned forward, bill slightly downtilted. One or both of the pair often call, using the 'kruk' call.

Meanwhile, the female stands with her head also slightly bowed and tilted away from the male. If she is not yet ready to respond, she will turn around as he walks, always facing him. Later, she moves back or performs the erect posture, wings down, tail up, head and bill strained upwards and pointing at the sky. In this pose she may walk around the male, who stops his parading and also adopts the upright, head-up pose, although without quite the same extreme intensity.

What happens next depends on the female. She may calm down and lower her head, in which case the male continues his parade. If not, the two stand together, heads up.

The reactions of the two birds to each other develop as time goes on. Once the pair is well established, so the stereotyped, ritualistic action and reaction becomes reduced, and a mere hint of recognition is all that takes place. If a bird returns to the nest, his mate may merely raise the bill a touch, a faint echo of the erect posture so strongly assumed earlier on in the affair.

If the male has a fish, a teasing, coy performance ensues. The female moves forward and attempts to take the fish that seems to be offered. But the male wants a little more yet and makes sure that the female does not grab the fish without further posturing. Sometimes it may be that a female has a fish and the male takes on the female role until he snatches the fish, at which point the roles are reversed to the norm once again, and he uses the same fish to court her.

Should there not be a fish, the parade phase is followed by the making of a nest scrape. The male initiates this, advertising the fact that he has a territory and that the female would do well to take advantage of it. The scrape is made by the tern leaning forward until his breast touches the ground. Then he can rest his weight on his chest, while using his feet to scrape and kick backwards, creating little spurts of sand and dust behind him.

The female may show interest by joining in the scraping. The male scrapes and moves, the female moves over to the same spot and scrapes some more. The male scrapes again, close by, and the female moves over to scrape on the same spot. This phase has been termed 'house hunting'. At the same time, the two give rather deep, growling calls,

A Common Tern making a nest first makes a scrape by leaning forward, scraping with its feet and rounding the hollow with its breast.

'kruu-krurr-krurr' or 'kerkerker', the so-called gurr-call. One of these initial, trial scrapes will eventually be used to hold the eggs.

The courtship activities on the ground are rather irregular and variable, with a pattern that is often altered by the actions of one or both birds rather than any fixed, unchanging sequence. The displays that lead to mating are more definite.

The male often walks in front of the female, in little circles or three-quarter circles ('horseshoes'), with his neck upstretched, head pushed forward and wings tightly closed. The wings are thus unlike the drooped wings of the bent posture or the slightly open wings of the erect posture. Now the male looks sleek and tight. The female may be aggressive and move away. If more responsive, she adopts a submissive pose and gives a distinctive begging call, a shrill, rather hoarse 'ki-ki-ki', the same note used when begging for a fish. The hunched posture at this point consists of a horizontal crouch, with the head held low but pulled back into the shoulders. Between calls the female's bill is held open.

Courtship feeding often, but not always, precedes mating. Some females, even when already paired, may accept a fish from a strange, intruder male and mate with him. The progression towards copulation is often faltering and likely to be aborted at first, although it is begun well before any eggs are laid. If successful, the female calls more intensely and hunches down more deeply, and the male sees his opportunity when his mate stays still and crouches. He mounts and copulates two or three times, remaining on the hen's back for anything up to three minutes if the pair is left undisturbed.

Once the male steps down to the ground, the two adopt a particularly tense, extreme version of the erect posture, heads stretched right up and bills vertical. Then they settle and begin to preen. If the sequence has been broken at an earlier stage, or if the male mounts but fails to copulate, the whole ritual begins again.

Courtship feeding

Courtship feeding, which may have played a small part in the ritual immediately before mating, now has a more important role. When it occurs, the female sees a male with a fish and begins to beg. The male may give her the fish, but then beg for it back again, and the sequence is repeated. Normally, however, the fish is eventually handed over and the female eats it. In earlier displays and especially the aerial excitement over the colony, which often involves the male carrying a silvery fish in his bill, the fish is little more than a symbol, an object of importance in the display but no more. Now, the female really does need the nourishment of the extra food.

She has the large, nutrient-rich eggs to produce and any extra fish from the male helps. So the male feeds the female during the period when mating is regular, before the eggs are laid. Also, the pair moves away to a good feeding area for several days, perhaps as many as ten, and the male feeds his mate frequently. This 'honeymoon' period is clearly important in bringing the female into good condition and helping the development of the eggs. During this period both birds of the pair return to the territory occasionally, to reaffirm ownership, and they remain there at night.

Before the first egg is laid – as little as six hours or as much as six days before – the female returns to the territory for good and the male flies to and from the sea, feeding her with a healthy diet of fat fish. Until

The male feeds a fish to his mate in the pre-egg-laying stage of courtship.

the complete clutch has been laid, the female does little fishing for herself, relying on her mate. After a few days, however, the male begins to share the incubation of the eggs and the female feeds herself much more, courtship feeding being gradually phased out.

This courtship feeding has been studied in great detail by I.R. Taylor of the University of Edinburgh. He found that during courtship the males selected the largest and heaviest items they could carry to feed to the females. Each female could judge the ability of the male as a fisherman, and therefore his likely ability to feed the future family. Also, the male could ensure that his efforts to feed the female were efficient, saving on his expenditure of time and energy during the process.

Nisbet showed that the total weight of the clutch laid by a female increases with greater courtship feeding by the male, so there is no doubt that this feeding really is of more than symbolic value. Also, the weight of the third egg in large clutches was particularly related to the amount of feeding from the male. At the same time, the larger (heavier) the third egg is, the more likely it is to produce a successfully fledged chick.

Male terns normally carry just a single fish or shrimp to the female at one time. If she is on a nesting territory some way from the feeding area, he will clearly be committed to a lot of time and effort flying backwards and forwards from one to the other. Should he be able to ensure that he carried the biggest, most nutritious items of food, he would be cutting down the energy requirements in this lengthy chore.

Taylor studied the terns on the Ythan estuary, a long, largely sandy estuary in Grampian. He saw males carrying fish and displaying to females. He studied them in the next stage of courtship, when male and female were together at the feeding grounds and actual courtship feeding began. The terns were occupying feeding territories along the estuary at this time, at low tide. The females spent most of their time sitting on the mud, while the males hunted for food for their hens and themselves. If nutrition was the sole consideration, the females might be expected to be fishing as well, effectively doubling their potential intake of food, but this is not so. Perhaps they would use more energy fishing, and moving about to remain available to be fed by the males, than it would be worth.

Later, in the final courtship phase, the females were away on the breeding sites and the males were flying to and fro to support them. This was studied at high tide, when spring tides brought many fish into the estuary. Taylor identified prey as often as possible and also estimated their lengths by comparison with the terns' bills. He caught some fish himself and measured their length and weight.

At low tide the terns fed on bottom-living crustacea and fish, especially the common shrimp and the viviparous blenny. Nearly all of the shrimps and other, tiny, unidentified items were eaten by the males themselves. Most of the fish, though, were carried to the females.

The viviparous blenny was, therefore, the commonest item fed to the females and, on average, this was twice as long and more than twice the weight of a shrimp.

At high tide, marine, surface-living fish were caught as they were swept into the estuary. These were largely tiny herrings under a year old and sandeels. Taylor found that 30 per cent of the catch was herring and 70 per cent sandeels. But 90 per cent of the food eaten by the males was sandeels – the long, thin, lightweight catch. About 66 per cent of the food delivered to females was composed of shorter, fatter, heavier herrings; and, even if sandeels were delivered, they were bigger than the ones eaten by the males. The average weight of an item eaten by the female was 2·29 g, while that eaten by the male was a mere 0·29 g. Taylor's intensive study is a fine example of the kind of hard, lengthy slog that produces fascinating and exciting results.

Nisbet showed that individual males varied in their ability to provide food for females. It may be that the poorer providers were unable to select the bigger food items to take back to the hens. Courtship feeding may, therefore, allow the females to judge the capabilities of the males as providers of food for the family. This, however, does not take much account of the fact that many pairs arrive at the colony already part-way through the courtship process and, of course, that most experienced terns return to the same breeding site year after year. Also, Taylor suggests, this selection of 'good' males, to be of any real significance, could take place only in the second and third phases of courtship; once that stage has been reached, it is, in any case, rather too late for the female to stop and look for another mate. The 'better' ones would, by then, all be spoken for anyway.

David Wiggins and Ralph D. Morris, students of terns in Canada, looked at courtship feeding in a different light. They studied the timing of such feeding and mating (copulatory) behaviour before and during egg-laying. They found that courtship feeding did not affect the likelihood of successful copulation, nor the number of copulations per mounting by the male. Nor did courtship feeding appear to initiate mounting. The 'box of chocolates' strategy seems to have no bearing on mating behaviour: even bigger fish fed to the female had no effect on the number or success of mating attempts.

10

NESTS, EGGS AND CHICKS

Nests and eggs

THE nest of a Common Tern is often little more than a shallow depression in soft sand. It is always on the ground, usually in an open situation, but it can be in more or less dense vegetation or among broken rocks and large stones.

A study of Common Terns nesting in Poland revealed that over half (45 of 83) nests made were on bare ground or in the scantiest, lowest scraps of vegetation. There were thirty nests on floating vegetation, just three beside a tussock of grass, three against prominent stones or stumps, and two in higher vegetation that screened them from sight.

On beaches, Common Terns may choose to nest on bare sand, or on shingle or gravel, whether small, discrete lines or ridges within a sandy tract or as complete beaches or headlands of small stones. Some nest on rocky islets and choose sites in irregular, broken ground, limited by the number of natural hollows or crevices in the rock. On the same cluster of rocks there may be nesting Common Gulls and Eiders, with Rock Pipits building their neat little cup-shaped nests in deep, narrow clefts among the sea pinks, scurvygrass and orange lichen.

Inland-nesting terns frequently (sensibly) choose island sites in flooded gravel pits (unless they are provided with artificial rafts specially for the purpose). I have watched them settling down at the beginning of the season on a rather bare earth slope, with a hint of green haze as new grass began to grow, but by the end of the season become all but invisible in deep vegetation. These gravel-pit islands are also used by nesting Black-headed Gulls, Greylag and Canada Geese, Mute Swans and Lapwings.

The nest itself is shallow and saucer-like. It may be entirely unlined, as are the majority of scrapes in sand, or lined with bits and pieces from the surrounding ground, whether of leaves and stems or of stones and shells. Again in Poland, of 53 nests recorded, two were unlined, fifteen had a slender rim of material but nothing else, 31 had both a rim and a thin, insubstantial lining, and five had a thick, dense pad of material in the bed of the nest.

The diameter of the nest varies according to the materials used and can be as little as 11·5 cm or as much as 24 cm. The inside of the

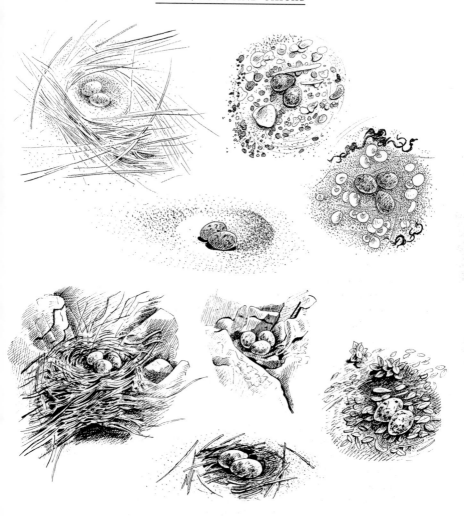

Nests vary greatly according to the immediate surroundings.

scrape averages 10 cm wide and 4 cm deep. Once the pair has settled on a particular scrape, the eggs are laid, but more desultory work may continue on the nest during incubation, with odd bits of vegetation or pebbles added to the rim or lining. A curious, unvarying ritual when the pair changes over at the nest also adds more to the nest rim from the surrounding ground.

A simple, shallow, scraped nest in loose sand is easily made. The bird leans forward, breast to the ground, and slowly rotates, kicking sand back with its feet as it goes. A little more smoothing of the resultant hollow and the nest is ready. A problem that affects all tern nests,

Sandy beaches and dunes are classic nesting sites for Common Terns.

but this sort in particular, is drifting sand, and a good wind may practically swamp a nest and its eggs. Loose sand always tends to run down the sides of the hollow, anyway, and gradually the little dent in an otherwise featureless sandy beach is worked on by wind, rain and drying sun until it would disappear without regular attention by the birds. Sitting birds on windy days always seem to be struggling against the odds to keep the nest clear of blown sand. Little Terns are particularly susceptible to it, but Common Terns also suffer from blown sand and sometimes fail in their nesting attempts because of it.

There is, however, a complete range of variation between the simple hollow and a substantial nest. Many pairs, as the Marples verified, make no effort at all to build anything into or around the nest cup, and it is not normal for a scanty or non-existent nest to be built up gradually during incubation. It simply stays bare throughout. But there may well be some small addition and reconstruction of material in a nest that has a rim of pebbles or shells or bits of dry marram stems. Others are enhanced by the wind blowing leaves and twigs against the incubating tern and creating a slight eminence on the open beach.

Some pairs build up a sizeable and quite well-made nest even before the eggs are laid. The materials are often picked from the surrounding area and more or less thrown into place, with an air of irritable, fidgety and almost aimless activity that somehow results in a nest that looks better than might have been intended. Other Common Terns, however, have a more determined and organized approach and will even carry nesting material from the mainland out to an island site.

It is possible, on marshy sites, that the nests that are built first are those on drier, higher places, and that lower, wetter sites are later additions and more built-up to resist possible flooding. There is little obvious correlation between site and structure, except that most nests are made of local materials, so that dune sites are more likely to have marram stalks and dwarf willow leaves, beach sites pebbles and shells.

Materials do vary, though, and all kinds of flotsam can be found in Common Terns' nests, from dried seaweed to twigs, feathers, bits of light wood and washed-up, fragmented pieces of plastic or polystyrene.

At least in some of the larger colonies, although it may be partly brought about through topographical influence, nests within a colony are more or less clumped into sub-groups, although this is not so strong a feature of Common Tern colonies as it is in Sandwich terneries. In some cases it seems that nests within the smaller clusters within a colony are better synchronized with each other (in terms of the breeding cycle) than with pairs elsewhere in the colony as a whole. This has already been mentioned, a function of the stimuli provided by courting pairs to other pairs in the immediate vicinity.

There is little variation in the timing of the nesting season through the European range of the Common Tern. Nesting usually begins in early May, with eggs rather few in the second week and laid mainly about the third week of the month. Older birds lay earlier than young ones.

The eggs themselves are smooth, but not highly glossed. The basic, underlying colour ('ground colour') is cream or buff, more or less tinged with yellow, green, blue or olive. On this pastel shade, a varied pattern

---

A typical clutch may be of three or four eggs, which are spotted and blotched.

of spots, blotches, streaks and lines of darker colours is superimposed. There are grey blobs as well as finer, blacker or browner markings, spread rather evenly over the whole egg. The effect is to create a well-camouflaged set of eggs, with sufficient irregularity in the pattern visually to break up the smooth outline and make them much harder to spot.

A smooth, uniformly coloured egg, even on a background of the same colour, is easier to see because it 'stands out' by virtue of the play of light and shade over its oval surface. The blotches and streaks of a patterned one counteract the smooth highlights and shadows, so no obvious egg shapes are visible.

While in some colonies the eggs may all take on a fairly similar appearance, others are recorded where every variety is present and the whole effect is extremely diverse. It has been said that, in Britain, east-coast colonies tend to produce greenish eggs while west-coast colonies frequently have a stone or buff base colour. As the incubation period progresses, so the eggs often fade in colour and the greener ones tend towards a bleached stone colour, anyway. There are occasional unmarked, often blue eggs, sometimes almost white ones, or unusually dark examples. Erythristic eggs, with a much greater red pigmentation than normal, are rare but not exceptional. At Wells-next-the-Sea, in Norfolk, one nest was said to have unspotted red eggs for seventeen successive years, until the hen bird was killed by a stoat.

The eggs vary from a rather broad oval, not unlike a small hen's egg, to a narrower form with a more marked 'pointed end'. They average 41 mm long by 31 mm wide, but the variation is considerable. Length may be from 35–48 mm and width from 27–33 mm. The weight of a fresh egg is around 21 g. In clutches of two eggs, the second is slightly smaller. In clutches of three, the third is a little more obviously the smallest. In one study, for example, weights of first, second and third eggs averaged, respectively, 21·5 g, 21·3 g and 20·8 g. Egg weight is related to the amount of fish eaten by the female (especially the amount fed to her by the male) before laying, as has already been discussed, and the size of the egg influences the likelihood of its hatching and producing a successfully fledged young bird, as will be shown later.

Arctic Terns' eggs are remarkably similar to those of Common Terns, both in overall appearance and in size, and the two are not safely distinguishable.

The number of eggs in a clutch – that is the number laid and incubated together by a single female – varies from colony to colony. It is almost always one, two or three, but the clutch size is not entirely predictable.

In England, of 420 Common Tern clutches, 4 per cent had one egg, 37 per cent had two and 59 per cent three, giving a mean of 2·65. In another study, there were 177 clutches of one egg, 685 of two, 1203 of three, and 23 of four, so 59·2 per cent had three eggs and the mean was 2·51. In Orkney and Shetland, of 143 clutches, the mean was 2·55. Of 151 clutches reported in West Germany, the mean was 2·84, while a much larger sample of 1588 in southern Russia gave a mean of 2·88; in the latter region, there were clutches of four (2 per cent) and even five (0·1 per cent) recorded.

It has been shown that some clutches of four eggs have certainly been laid by a single female, but it is likely that others of four, and certainly the very rare ones of five, have been produced by two females laying in the same nest. Not only do the older, experienced birds lay a little earlier than young birds, but they also tend to lay larger clutches, on average.

The period of time between the laying of the first egg and subsequent ones varies according to the size of the clutch. In clutches of just two eggs, they may be laid less than twelve hours apart. If there are to be three eggs, there is usually about a day between the first and second, then a delay of two days before the third. To produce these large, rich eggs is clearly an effort for the female, and the extra nourishment she receives from the male in the form of courtship feeding is crucially important.

Incubation

If the eggs are incubated consistently, they hatch within 21 or 22 days. If the parent birds are frequently disturbed, especially at night when predators can keep them away for lengthy spells, the period increases to 25 or more days, even 31 days in some recorded cases. The first eggs are not fully incubated until the clutch is complete. There is no great disparity in the age of chicks within a brood as there is, for example in many owls, and diurnal birds of prey.

Both parents incubate the eggs but the female takes the bigger part, around 75 per cent of the incubation in the early stages especially. The changeover may be seen about seven times a day. Usually, if the female is sitting, the male appears carrying a fish and calling with his advertising call. Landing near the nest, he then walks in, head low, sometimes giving the quieter 'kruk' call. The hen will beg, even if the male has no fish in his bill, with typical shrill, short, quick notes. She quickly rises from the eggs and moves alongside the male, who feeds her. Before leaving the eggs, the sitting bird will pick up a nearby pebble or other object and throw it back over one shoulder, incidentally helping to reinforce the rim of the nest hollow.

In the later stages this nest-relief ritual is sometimes dispensed with. The incoming bird does little more than raise his wings as he alights and the female stands to allow him to take over on the eggs. As the outgoing bird flies off, it will almost invariably give a sharp 'kip' note.

Quite frequently the off-duty mate will stand in the territory with the sitting bird and even preen the wingtips and tail of the bird on the eggs. At the same time it may be distracted and squabble with the neighbours, so, with such activities repeated all through, the colony is all noise and activity.

The sitting tern appears to recognize the call of its incoming mate long before it arrives, but is more or less indifferent to the everyday activities of other terns passing overhead. The birds sit tight and rarely leave the eggs except at the changeover period. An old belief that terns do not incubate during the day, but leave the eggs open to the warmth of the sun, is hard to explain.

The incubating tern often moves the eggs with its beak, rolling them slightly and shuffling to get comfortable once more. As the eggs begin to hatch, such attention becomes more frequent and the parent gives an impression of some unease, or excitement, or at least an interest in what is going to happen next. The shell begins to crack with a pattern of fine, radiating lines across the middle, then a larger split appears and the chick struggles out.

Even before this, the chick may be heard calling faintly from within the egg, and slight tapping sounds can be detected. The chick uses a tiny, flat, white 'egg-tooth' at the tip of the bill as its means of escape. After about three days this egg-tooth (and a tiny tooth on the lower mandible, too) falls away, no longer of any use.

The parent bird does not help the chick in its struggle to break free of the egg. Instead, it seizes the eggshell as soon as it is free and flies off with it, to drop it well clear of the colony. This removes the eyecatching, telltale shell with its pale inner surface, to reduce danger from sharp-eyed predators.

An egg about to hatch, with a newly hatched chick already dry.

The Marples weighed twelve eggs before they hatched and found an average of just 18·18 g. The average weight of the chicks was 13·91 g, varying from 11·73–16·95 g. Other chicks weighed on the day they hatched were as light as 9·57 g. Of thirty chicks weighed, the average change in weight during their first day was a loss of 4·9 g. Starved chicks found dead after three days weighed just 11·3 g.

The chicks

The chick starts life outside the egg bedraggled and wet. Brooding by the parent helps the down to dry out within a few hours. The chick then becomes a wonderful, clumsy, and engaging bundle of fluff.

The pattern on the down of a young chick varies, but essentially it is fawn, pale brown or even rather gingery, with black or dark brown marks. The dark pattern is nearly symmetrical, around a central line along the head and back. The head has some central spots and often a row of spots either side, or a circle of spots around the crown. The back has lines or elongated spots just each side of the central line, more or less parallel or diverging into a 'V' or diamond. On the hind end of the chick are more, smaller, spots and the bases of the rudimentary wings are blotched. Underneath, there are also spots about the thighs. The throat is dark, but the rest of the underside clear white. The tiny feet are pink, orange-pink or orange-yellow, as is the inside of the mouth.

The Arctic Tern chick is very much the same, but has a pale or dark grey colour to the flanks and rump, which is generally a good distinction in a mixed colony.

The colour of the egg has no bearing on the colour or tone of the chick. Dark chicks appear from pale eggs and vice versa. A dark chick and a light chick may hatch from a clutch of two identical eggs.

The chick quickly senses that it needs to be fed and that the big, white creature beside it, with a fearsome-looking bill, is the most likely source of food. This is all instinctive, of course, with no conscious thought behind it. The red of the parent's bill must act as a stimulus, and the chick in turn stimulates its parent by pecking at the bill tip. The chick makes weak, cheeping, food-begging noises, but these play little part in the process at first and it is only when the downy hatchling is two days old that proper and effective begging calls are heard.

Pecking at the bill either makes the adult feed the chick or it settles down to brood it. As important as being fed, the chick must be kept warm (or, indeed, sheltered from baking hot sun). If it is really hot and the sun is burning down on to the bare sandy beach, the chick is in danger of succumbing to heatstroke. The parents are ready for this and have been recorded flying to the sea to wet their body feathers, then returning to cool the chick using this salty moisture. The two adults take it in turns to do this, one staying with the chick and perhaps shading it, the other flying off to find water.

The male does most of the fishing to feed the chick in the first few days and also, later, tends to fly farther afield than the female when hunting. Food is carried back in the bill, a risky business if there are Arctic Skuas or large gulls about. If the tern manages to avoid these, it returns with a fish that is roughly appropriate for the size of the chick, although sometimes the fish offered are too big for the chick to handle. Nevertheless, the tiny, downy creature can somehow get down a fish almost as long as itself, occasionally sitting back, eyes closed, belly bursting, with the tail of the fish still hanging out of its half-open bill.

The parent terns quickly learn to recognize their own young, and do so without problems by the second day. The chick, meanwhile, is quick to learn the individual qualities of the calls of its parents and, by the fourth day, it reacts strongly to the advertising calls of its parents, given before they can be seen as they approach the nest with a fish.

Downy Common Tern chicks are hard to distinguish from those of other terns.

If they are left alone, the young chicks scamper off into the nearest scrap of vegetation or patch of broken rocks, if there is such cover available. If not, they may make shallow scrapes which offer them some shelter from the wind and sun. The calls of their parents bring them out into the open, ready to be fed.

At this stage there may be many chicks left alone, waiting for the arrival of a parent bird with food. When one is fed and the parent leaves to find further supplies, it may be at risk from older chicks 'next door'. Many Common Tern chicks supplement the food they get from their parents by fish stolen from younger, smaller chicks nearby.

If the chick is offered a large, difficult fish and drops it into sticky, clinging sand, the parent may retrieve it and take it back to the water's edge to wash it, before returning and starting again. The size of prey and sometimes also the species of fish caught for the chicks vary according to the age of the youngsters. Terns feed larger fish to chicks more than a week or so old than to the tiny, downy creatures just out of the egg. In one study, older chicks were fed more sticklebacks than younger ones. In Northumberland, it was found that young chicks were fed a diet of sandeels while older ones received more small herrings and sprats.

As the chicks grow, so the fish offered to them become larger than those eaten by the parents, which make do with small fry while ensuring the best possible diet for their offspring.

Various observations have been made on the number of feeds received by Common Tern chicks. At one colony, single chicks received fifteen feeds per day, at 0·8 feeds per hour. Broods of two had 23 feeds at 1·8 per hour, and broods of three chicks were fed 38 times per day, at 2·1 feeds per hour. Bigger broods clearly work the parent terns much harder, as they increase the number of visits to the nest with food, although each chick receives proportionately fewer visits per day.

The number of visits depends on the local topography and the species of prey being captured. In Virginia, USA, a colony eating fish fed broods of three chicks about four times per hour. In the Black Sea, where a third of the diet was shrimps, broods of three received just one to 1·6 feeds per hour. Small, invertebrate prey in other studies produced higher feeding rates. In Finland, the average intake per chick was 798 g between hatching and fledging around 25 days later, around 32 g per day on average.

Anti-predator behaviour

Young terns unable to fly are extremely vulnerable to predators, particularly as they are so often on open ground with no shelter available in the event of danger. Adults are constantly on guard, and a sharp 'kip' call or loud 'keee-arrr' is enough to make even the smallest chick crouch motionless, pressed down into the ground. The spotted pattern of the down and the immobility of the chick are the essential elements of its defence.

After a few days, the chicks tend to separate and, if there is a danger warning, they crouch outside the nest beside any bit of cover or small feature available, so that their outline is further confused and broken up both by their own patterning and by the minor irregularities of their surroundings. A piece of wood, a heap of feathers, a scattering of shells, all offer the more broken background against which a 'freezing' tern chick is more likely to remain undetected.

Once the chick is a dozen or so days old, it may make more active efforts to avoid predators, such as making a dash for the safety of the sea or flooded pit if the water is within reach.

This pair of Common Tern chicks would be well camouflaged if viewed from a few yards away.

Whatever the chick does, it can only hope to capitalize on the anti-predator actions of its parents and, indeed, all the other adults of the colony. The parents, while warning the chick to keep quiet and keep still, do their very best to drive off whatever danger threatens the young. This, in reality, depends on their ability to see what the potential predator is up to. If the colony is approached at night, the adults might decide that discretion is the best course and simply leave. They do this if they are still on eggs, which, if the eggs survive, extends the incubation period because of the lengthy 'cold' spells which retard the development of the embryo.

By day, though, the terns feel more confident, and they can at least use their aerial dexterity to the full in both attacking and avoiding a predator. The colony can also act in concert and give even a formidable predator a pretty hard time.

Anything like a fox, a hedgehog, a stoat or a mink, even a human, is likely to be subjected to a torrent of abuse and a rain of steep, intimidating dives by screeching birds. The adults of the colony hang in the air above the threat, calling and wheeling about, and take it in turns to dive down one or two at a time. They mean business, too.

Although fewer people get hit by Common Terns than by Arctic Terns, Commons are capable of striking and their strong, sharply pointed bills are weapons to be respected. They often draw blood, and smaller predators sometimes succumb to constant bombardment by the terns. Others retreat, tails between their legs, seen off by the screaming, whirling crowd.

Intruding humans, often people who are ignorant of the presence of a tern colony, find themselves involuntarily flinching and ducking as the terns dash down in literally hair-raising stoops, their wings ripping noisily through the air at the bottom of each dive, each swoop accompanied by a loud, jarring chatter and scream, 'chakakakakakaarrrrr!'.

Not only do the terns strike home with their bills, they sometimes make contact with body and feet and, with enough regularity for it not to be a chance occurrence, they spatter the offending visitor with liquid excrement, too. The force of the blows was described by the indomitable Marples, who suffered many cuts with blood drawn from head wounds even through a thick tweed cap. One of them was struck a dozen times in quick succession by a pair of Common Terns, although they confirmed that Arctics are the most courageous, or ill-tempered, terns, a pair of which hit George Marples 28 times before he could gain neutral ground.

At least against human intruders, individual terns vary in their aggression. It is when eggs are about to hatch or there are very small chicks that they are generally the most spiteful in their attacks.

Passing gulls, crows, Kestrels and Buzzards are also chased and buffeted in the air, whether intent on mischief or simply innocent victims. Adult Herring Gulls appear to learn the dangers, or at least discomforts, of flying across a tern colony, although young ones, perhaps wandering and new to the area, seem more often to fall into the trap of triggering off an assault. The terns are generally well able to gain height, dive and climb again for a further assault, and nimble enough to avoid any danger should the tables be turned. Against a serious predator such as a Peregrine, however, such mobbing is always a dangerous game.

11

PREDATORS
AND PRODUCTIVITY

THE productivity of a pair of Common Terns is largely decided well before their chicks hatch out, new and downy, into the world. At least, the potential is partly mapped out. The actual achievement depends, then, on all kinds of factors: weather; survival of the adults; the availability of sufficient food; the presence of predators, and the communal ability of the colony to discourage them. It is, however, the abilities of the parents and their pre-breeding behaviour, especially the courtship feeding of the female by the male, that influence later results.

It has already been suggested that a female might 'test' or judge a male and choose her mate according to the extent to which a male could meet his parental obligations. We have seen, however, that, if a female really does judge a male by his attentiveness and ability to catch a lot of fish with which to tempt her, she is left in a very tricky situation indeed if he does not come up to scratch. If the female 'decides' that this male is not made of the stuff that she wants as the father of her chicks, what happens next? All the 'good' males are, by then, snapped up.

In any case, we have already seen that many pairs of terns arrive at the colony already paired, after some sort of courtship on the way back from Africa. Does a form of testing take place then? If so, why aren't the top males surrounded by squabbling females fighting for their favours?

Also, most pairs resume the partnerships of earlier years, so the testing theory may be valid only during the first year or two of breeding, when young birds are still not so likely to show fidelity to mate and site as older ones. Do the older pairs remain faithful to *each other*, or are they faithful to a *nest site* that has proved successful in the past, thus meeting up, almost incidentally, with their past partner if he or she has also survived the winter?

Certainly, each spring sees a renewal of courtship behaviour and territorial defence, and there are no half-hearted measures whether the pair consists of old, established partners or not. The pair-bonding and the courtship feeding, which helps so much to produce a good set of eggs, go on year after year, as strong as ever.

Unless there is some unexpected factor (for example, a sudden storm), ninety per cent of eggs hatch. That is a good rate, a testament in part to the careful and attentive presence of the adult terns at their nest and the abilities of flocks of terns to deter would-be predators.

In England, of 420 broods studied, 69 per cent of the chicks that hatched survived until they fledged. Where there was a single chick, the fledging success was 62 per cent. With two chicks, success was 84 per cent for the first chick, and 57 per cent for the second. For broods of three, the success rate of first chicks was raised still further, to 89 per cent, that of the second to 77 per cent but the fledging rate of third chicks was a mere 22 per cent.

Of the chicks that died before they fledged (that is before they were able to fly), 80 per cent died in the first five days after hatching. The second and third chicks died at a younger age than first chicks, again confirming the greater strength and fitness of the first-born. The main cause of death was starvation. This neatly fits the idea that older chicks in a brood have a better chance of survival than younger ones, but it also shows that first chicks have a better chance of survival in a brood of two or three than in a brood of one.

In studies in New York, it was shown that six-year-old terns fledged 0·83 young per pair, while seven-year-old pairs raised 1·03 per pair, a respectable difference in accordance with our argument that older birds are 'better' breeders than young ones.

Overall, the productivity of terns varies greatly from year to year, and some colonies occasionally fail altogether. On average, however, it was found in the USA that 0·9 young could be expected for every pair of Common Terns that laid eggs.

Common Terns lay eggs over a period of a day or several days, but, if they have more than one egg, they do not begin to incubate properly

Common Terns carrying fish are frequently harried by Arctic Skuas.

until two or three eggs have been laid. This means that, assuming each egg takes the same length of incubation time to hatch, the eggs will hatch out close together, in terms of time, and not several days apart. Nevertheless, there is usually *some* delay, and this is crucial to each chick's prospects for survival.

The difference in time of hatching is important in that it affects the likelihood of the younger chicks getting fed. When a parent arrives with a fish, the older, stronger, larger chick naturally elbows aside its smaller siblings and takes the lion's share of the food. If food is short, the older chick may survive at the expense of the younger, weaker ones, which simply starve.

The incubation of an egg requires steady attention over many days, from a devoted pair of terns that are both willing to sit on the eggs and turn them when necessary. The attentiveness of the parents may, according to I.C.T. Nisbet and M.E. Cohen, depend on their age and experience as well as outside, environmental considerations.

Nisbet and Cohen studied Common Terns, and assumed that their breeding strategy had evolved so that the investment of time and energy in each egg by the parent birds was adjusted to the relative probability of successfully raising young from them. In other words, the terns are likely to put most of their effort into the 'best' eggs and chicks, with the best chance of survival. Small, underweight eggs and sickly, runt chicks are likely to be more trouble than the final result is worth, unless food is so abundant and easily caught that even such poor raw materials can be turned into healthy, flying young terns.

Their studies were made in the early 1970s in Massachusetts. Early in the season, at least, hatching intervals of Common Tern eggs were shorter than laying intervals, as already explained (females tend to incubate first eggs intermittently, sitting tight at times but standing over it at others, so it will not be fully incubated until the second or even the third is laid). The general trend was for the delay between first and last eggs laid in a clutch to increase as the season drew on, so that early clutches tended to be more coherent in terms of age. The same was true for Roseate Terns. But the strength of the tendency for laying intervals to increase later in the season varied from colony to colony. The implication, though, is that 'getting down to it' early is better than arriving at a colony late and beating about the bush. Dithering by newly formed, young pairs will do nothing for their productivity.

The tendency for the eggs in a single clutch to hatch out at different times (so strongly shown in certain owls, for example) is considered to be an adaptation to an irregular food supply. If food is scarce, the bigger, older chicks survive and there need be no wastage of food bestowed on

ABOVE *A pair of Common Terns at a typical nest with eggs in the lee of a sand dune.* BELOW *An adult brings a fish to its newly-hatched chick, which anticipates its arrival after recognizing its calls.*

Norman Arlott

the younger, smaller ones, which are already doomed. Should food be abundant, all the chicks stand a better chance. In Common Terns, it has indeed been shown that, in clutches of three eggs, the third chick is likely to survive only in years of particular plenty, or where the parent birds seem to be old, experienced and especially good at providing food.

Nevertheless, the third chick, or third egg, is useful in its way, because if the first or second gets eaten (say, by a passing gull), the third can take its place and fulfil its potential. Nisbet argues that a small, late egg may even stand a better chance of avoiding predation than a big, first-laid one (the one to take the fancy of a casual predator perhaps). Some terns lay 'odd' eggs, and I have seen Black-headed Gull eggs that stood out, almost unmarked, pale blue, among the general run of well-camouflaged brown. Maybe these are also liable to attract the eye of a predator. While the small *egg* might survive, a small, late *chick* stands the least chance of getting enough to eat unless its older siblings die.

The argument goes, therefore, that, when prospects are really good, the chances of raising a chick from the third egg are improved and the terns should delay incubation of the first and second, so that all three hatch close together. If the season is a bad one, or breeding too long delayed, then the terns should start incubation right away, keeping the third egg 'in reserve' as a replacement, but not really having much chance of rearing three chicks.

Nisbet and Cohen showed that this did happen with their Common Terns. As the season went on, so the interval between hatchings increased and so, also, the third egg became relatively smaller. By the end of the laying season, few terns laid a third egg at all. This would match the argument if the food supply declined through the season,

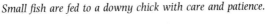

Small fish are fed to a downy chick with care and patience.

making later clutches less viable than early ones. Remember that old, established pairs arrive first at the colony and lay earlier than new, young ones, and that they do best.

There was no measurement of food availability, but it was shown that chicks grew more slowly if they hatched later in the season than those that were early. This might mean that food was less abundant, or harder to catch, or that the parents simply got tired and performed less well. Also, it involves the younger, less experienced birds among those pairs whose chicks grew more slowly.

Wiggins and Morris studied the parental care of Common Terns. Females take a greater share of the incubation, although both sexes spent about the same amount of time at the nest while there were eggs. Once the eggs hatched, females spent a greater amount of time at the nest than the males. Males then fed the chicks about three times more than the females. Interestingly, females tended to bring fish of the same size throughout the fledging period. Males, on the other hand, began with small fish and gradually brought larger ones as the chicks grew.

Wiggins and Morris concluded that the courtship feeding of the female by the male (vitally important in producing large, viable eggs) and the feeding of the chicks by the male were more important than the attentiveness of the female. It had earlier been assumed that the investment of time and energy in the eggs and young by the female was greater than that by the male, who, after all, did little compared with the egg-laying efforts of his mate. Common Terns lay three eggs which total around 45 per cent of the female's body weight, so her investment in them is certainly high. On the other hand, the males are busy catching fish to feed themselves and their mates, and in several seabird species it has been shown that males lose more weight than females in the egg-laying period. The parental contribution by the male, who also spends much time defending the territory, seems to be at least as great as that of the female.

The chances of an egg hatching and a chick fledging depend on more than the good start given by a busy male feeding his mate so that she can lay a big egg. Predators play a major role.

Predation and other factors

In the Great Lakes area of North America, Common Terns are in decline. Studies of their colonies attempted to elucidate the reasons behind this long-term fall in numbers. On Gull Island, there were up to 1500 pairs of Common Terns in 1933, 676 in 1976 and 242 in 1986. Many pairs moved to Little Pelican Island. On this island, however, Turnstones (surprisingly), Ring-billed Gulls, Herring Gulls and mink were all likely predators.

Turnstones punctured the eggs and ate their contents. Quite often, a Turnstone would break one egg and the terns would react as if it had hatched. So preoccupied were they in collecting and removing the broken eggshell (the normal reaction to reduce the conspicuousness of the nest to predators) that the Turnstone would easily move in and eat the second and third eggs, too. This neatly illustrates the degree to which even seemingly 'intelligent' acts (such as eggshell removal) by the terns are pre-programmed reactions to particular stimuli, even if the results are ridiculously inappropriate.

Herring Gulls ate eggs whole, carrying them off or simply swinging their head and bill upwards and cracking the eggs at the nest. Ring-billed Gulls, however, were not seen to take eggs.

At this colony, neither Turnstones nor gulls were apparently attacked by the terns, although in England even a passing Black-headed Gull is likely to be beaten off in no uncertain terms. The Turnstones responsible for egg theft were still awaiting the thaw of northern ice and soon moved off to their own breeding grounds in the Arctic. After this, the terns could re-lay and fare better.

Once the chicks were hatched, they became extremely vulnerable to mink. I have seen photographs of tern colonies in Scotland, with whole rows of dead chicks killed by mink and, with little doubt in some instances, by otters. The surviving chicks in the North American study were mostly those that were hidden away in long vegetation.

Another problem was the movement of sand and shingle, the basis of the colony itself. Some of it was overgrown by vegetation, while other areas were swept away by winds and waves. Also, the numbers of Ring-billed Gulls, which might have taken more eggs and chicks had the researchers not incidentally kept them away, but which undoubtedly competed for space, kept down the numbers of Common Terns.

The Marples reported the damaging effects of bad weather upon terns. Cold, wet spells in June frequently chilled eggs and made it difficult for the parents to keep their tiny chicks warm and dry. Worst of all, a cold spell accompanied by a strong wind often means that eggs are buried and chicks are swamped, choked and killed in great numbers.

The unaccountable loss of food was also noted by the Marples, and it was a greater killer than the weather. The run of disastrous seasons in the Shetlands in the 1980s caused a great decline in Arctic Terns; these periods coincided with a sudden fall in numbers of sandeels and this may have been linked with overfishing but also with changes in sandeel distribution. The Marples noted Common Terns failing every few years because of the failure of the expected herring crop, and young terns would die wholesale, even if they were almost ready to fly.

At Salthouse, in 1924, half the chicks died. At Scolt Head, in 1925, gales and rain destroyed many eggs and chicks; in the following year, at the same place, many chicks died, and a quarter died at Salthouse in 1927 because of the weather. At Scolt Head in the latter year, over half the chicks died within a day of hatching, and at Blakeney, in 1929, hundreds died almost as they hatched. These catastrophes are normal for the terns and their breeding strategies can cope, but for the onlooker, especially the dedicated tern-watchers who struggle to protect them from predators and interference, the results are little short of heartbreaking.

I.C.T. Nisbet, in his Massachusetts studies, created a model for the declining Common Tern population there. He suggested that just 7 to 13 per cent of the fledged young survived to breed at four years old. After that, the annual mortality was 7·5–11 per cent from 1940 to 1956, increasing to 13–21 per cent from 1970 to 1975. At a New York colony, however, over 14 per cent survived to breed and the annual adult mortality was just 8 per cent. Perhaps this is a closer match to the norm, where Common Tern populations are stable.

Given a bit of luck, a Common Tern, once it has survived its first few years of life, has a few good seasons to look forward to. The oldest ringed bird was 25 years old. After all, the bird has only to succeed in rearing one young to breeding age to replace itself for the population to remain stable: a bit more than one, perhaps, as that offspring then also has to live long enough to replace itself, too. It does not seem much to ask, but, given the trials of a tern's life and the threats that face its eggs and chicks, it sometimes seems remarkable that it happens at all.

12

THE JUVENILE

THE feathers grown by a young tern while it is still close to the nest and, as yet, unable to fly serve it well for some months. They are its juvenile plumage, and most of the feathers of the wings and tail remain unchanged for about a year. By the following summer – in the tern's first-summer plumage – they are, naturally, somewhat worn, faded and bleached.

Why do young terns (and gulls) have plumages that are different from those of their parents? Terns, despite having such raucous and expressive calls, also live in a very visual world. The white bodies and underwings of the adults make them easily visible at great range. The long, vivid red stiletto bill is clearly of value in courtship and territorial displays and threatening behaviour. The full black cap, dipped forward to confront an intruder to the nest, is a strong and forceful expression of dominance in close-range encounters.

Adult terns at their nests are very territorial. Any other tern that strays into the nesting territory is likely to be threatened and attacked. The young tern perhaps looks different because it has to defuse this aggression, to take the edge off the involuntary response of its parents to the sight of another bird at their nest. Simply, it needs to avoid being pecked to death by its own parents.

Yet this cannot be a full explanation. It seems a good one, and probably holds good for many gulls. A young Kittiwake, for example, is obliged to sit on a tiny ledge above a dizzying drop and can hardly escape the aggression of one of its parents if it is attacked by mistake. So it has black bands across its wings and, very importantly, across the back of its neck. If need be, it can turn, to 'face away' and reveal the black bands, which seems to take the wind out of the sails of the potential chick-battering parent.

All the same, stray tern chicks which wander, while their own parents are away, into adjacent territories face instant rebuffs from neighbouring adults. Indeed, they can be hacked and pecked and buffeted until they die, and such wanderings are undertaken at their peril. Their 'different' plumage, with its brown barring and white forehead, is of no obvious value then.

It has often been remarked on how wonderful it is that a pair of terns can recognize their own stray youngsters, even among large numbers of, to us, practically identical chicks. But the chicks, although they react to the calls of their own parents, may mistake adults on the ground (or simply react in the 'correct' way to any adult), beg for food from the wrong ones and receive severe punishment in return.

The black cap is certainly important to a breeding adult tern. In the same way the brown hood of a Black-headed Gull is highly significant (as is the white nape, which has the opposite meaning and is turned to another gull in submission). In autumn, or even late summer in the gulls' case, it is the forehead that turns white first; in spring, it is the forehead that becomes solidly dark last. The dark frontal aspect, with its heavy meaning, is there for the shortest possible time. Sandwich Terns have the forehead all black for a few weeks at the most.

The young Common Tern has a pale forehead from the start and this probably helps to reduce the reaction to it by other, adult terns nearby and by its parents when it thrusts its bill towards them, anxious for a meal. But the brown bars on the back, the gingery wash on the forehead (it does not look gleaming white), the duskiness about the wings and tail, all are probably as much concerned with camouflage as with reducing aggression.

The juvenile has a neat pattern of dark subterminal marks and pale fringes to its upperpart feathers.

Young gulls, however, have a much stronger tendency towards cryptic plumage. Not, perhaps, the Kittiwake, which has nowhere to hide and looks strikingly black and white, but young Herring Gulls, Lesser Black-backed Gulls and Black-headed Gulls all have a lot of mottled brown about them. They are probably less conspicuous that way and more able to hide.

Back in their winter retreat, Black, Common, Roseate and Sandwich Terns join Royal Terns in Tema harbour, Ghana.

If there is no danger, though, young Common Terns growing their first set of feathers often stand about in the open and exercise their wings. They make little leaps into the air, flapping their wings. Eventually they may rise and drift away for 50 or 100 m, to crash-land ignominiously in the sand. By the time they are able to fly, they weigh on average 78 g and they are about a month old.

They can fly, they can swim and they take themselves off to the nearest water's edge, where they often assemble in sizeable groups. They are still fed by their respective parents, but begin to attempt a little fishing themselves.

They are fed by the parents in the air, with a fish passed from the bill of the adult to that of the juvenile, or on the ground, when the exchange is less dramatic but more reliable. They may also be fed as they sit on the sea. If fed on the ground or on the sea, the juvenile tern grasps the fish and then flies with it and swallows it a few seconds later.

At first the chicks wait for their parents to return to feed them, but, after four or five days, they begin to follow them on their fishing expeditions. This may be of value in observing their parents and 'learning' to fish, but it is clear that it is not a necessary stage in the development of a young tern. Young Sandwich Terns have been watched diving at flotsam on the sea, as if practising their dives. Skimmers, tern-like but very specialized, have a different feeding technique centred around their remarkable bills, in which the longer lower mandible performs a special function as it is dragged through the surface of the water while the bird flies. Young skimmers begin to practise only four days after fledging, with no parental accompaniment.

There are some remarkable reports of adults passing fish to their chicks underwater as if teaching the chicks to catch it (as a cheetah releases a young gazelle in front of its eager cubs). There are, though, plenty of observations of young terns diving for fish alone, and it is clear that they can do so successfully without parental teaching.

Nevertheless, Common Terns are fed by their parents for long periods in some instances. Young terns often stay with their parents on their first migration south and may still be fed by them some thousands of miles from the breeding colony. The period of parental care is greater, in general, for terns than for gulls, and this has been related to the more specialist feeding technique.

Eventually the young tern, born in a land of long summer days, lengthy twilight and short nights, finds itself in the tropics, where night comes early and fast and the temperature drops as if the rapidly setting sun triggers a switch. No longer do the sounds of Oystercatchers reverberate in its ears. No more can it see the green hills and grey rocks, the swathes of orange seaweed or the pale golden dunes of its first home. Instead, it is on a strange shore, where swaying palm trees line the beach and the air crackles with the electric notes of countless crickets and cicadas, throbs with the rhythmic calls of frogs every night. Here it will stay for months, probably more than a year, before it reacts to an irresistible urge to move back north one spring, to find the very same colony where it first learned to fly and to fish.

Select Bibliography

Brazil, Mark A., *The Birds of Japan*, Christopher Helm, London, 1991

Buckland, S.T., Bell, M.V., and Picozzi, N., *The Birds of North-East Scotland*, North-East Scotland Bird Club, Aberdeen, 1990

Cox, Simon, *A New Guide to the Birds of Essex*, Essex Bird Watching and Preservation Society, 1984

Cramp, Stanley, Bourne, W.R.P., and Saunders, David, *The Seabirds of Britain and Ireland*, Collins, London, 1974

Cramp, S., et al, *The Birds of the Western Palearctic, vol. IV*, Oxford University Press, Oxford, 1985

De Schauensee, R.M., and Phelps, W.H., *A Guide to the Birds of Venezuela*, Princeton University Press, Princeton, 1978

Dymond, J.N., *The Birds of Fair Isle*, Ritchie, Edinburgh, 1991

Fitter, R.S.R., and Richardson, R.A., *Collins Pocket Guide to British Birds*, Collins, London, 1952

Fuller, R.J., *Bird Habitats in Britain*, Poyser, Calton, 1982

Grant, P.J., and Scott, R.E., 'Field identification of juvenile Common, Arctic and Roseate Terns', *British Birds* 62 (1969), 297–9

Harrison, Colin, *An Atlas of the Birds of the Western Palaearctic*, Collins, London, 1982

Harrison, Graham R., Dean, Alan R., Richards, Alan J., and Smallshire, David, *The Birds of the West Midlands*, West Midland Bird Club, Studley, 1982

Hume, R.A., and Grant, P.J., 'The upperwing pattern of adult Common and Arctic Terns', *British Birds* 67 (1974), 133–6

Hutchinson, Clive D., *Birds in Ireland*, Poyser, Calton, 1989

Jonsson, Lars, *Birds of Sea and Coast*, Penguin, London, 1978

Kirkham, Ian R., and Nisbet, Ian C.T., 'Feeding techniques and field identification of Arctic, Common and Roseate Terns', *British Birds* 80 (1987), 41–7

Marples, George and Ann, *Sea Terns or Sea Swallows*, Country Life, London, 1934

Nelson, Bryan, *Seabirds: their biology and ecology*, Hamlyn, London, 1980

Nisbet, I.C.T., 'Courtship feeding, egg size and breeding success in Common Terns', *Nature* 241 (1973), 141–2

Nisbet, I.C.T., and Cohen, M.E., 'Asynchronous hatching in Common and Roseate Terns, *Sterna hirundo* and *S. dougallii*', *Ibis* 117 (1975), 374–9

Parslow, J.L.F., *The Breeding Birds of Britain and Ireland*, Poyser, Berkhamsted, 1973

Peterson, R.T., *A Field Guide to the Birds*, Houghton Mifflin, Boston, 1934 and 1980

Peterson, R.T., Mountfort, G., and Hollom, P.A.D., *A Field Guide to the Birds of Britain and Europe*, Collins, London, 1954 and 1966

Prater, A.J., *Estuary Birds of Britain and Ireland*, Poyser, Calton, 1981

Richardson, R.A., 'A distinction in flight between Arctic and Common Terns', *British Birds* 46 (1953), 411–12

Scott, R.E., and Grant, P.J., 'Uncompleted moult in *Sterna* terns and the problem of identification', *British Birds* 62 (1969), 93–7

Sharrock, J.T.R., *The Atlas of Breeding Birds in Britain and Ireland*, BTO, Tring, 1976

Taylor, D.W., Davenport, D.L. and Flegg, J.J.M., *The Birds of Kent*, Meresborough Books, Kent, 1984

Taylor, I.R., 'Prey selection during courtship feeding in the Common Tern', *Ornis Scandinavica* 10 (1979), 142–4

Thom, Valerie M., *Birds in Scotland*, Poyser, Calton, 1986

Thomas, G.J., 1982. 'Breeding Terns in Britain and Ireland, 1975–79', *Seabird Report no 6*

Urban, Emil K., *et al*, *The Birds of Africa, vol II*, Academic Press, London, 1986

Vande Weghe, J-P, 'La Sterne Pierregarin *Sterna hirundo* et la Sterne Arctique *Sterna paradisaea*: Identification et passage en Belgique', *Aves* 3 (1966), 1–5

Voous, K.H., *Birds of the Netherlands Antilles*, De Walburg Pers, 1983

Walpole-Bond, John, *A History of Sussex Birds*, Witherby, London, 1938

Wiggins, David A., and Morris, Ralph D., 'Parental care of the Common Tern *Sterna hirundo*', *Ibis* 129 (1987), 533-40

Scientific Names of Bird Species

All species of birds mentioned in the text are listed below, with their scientific name, in systematic order.

Red-throated Diver *Gavia stellata*
Great Northern Diver *Gavia immer*
Great Crested Grebe *Podiceps cristatus*
Brown Booby *Sula leucogaster*
Gannet *Morus bassanus*
Cormorant *Phalacrocorax carbo*
frigatebirds *Fregata* spp.
egrets *Egretta* spp.
Grey Heron *Ardea cinerea*
flamingoes *Phoenicopterus* spp.
Mute Swan *Cygnus olor*
Whooper Swan *Cygnus cygnus*
Greylag Goose *Anser anser*
Canada Goose *Branta canadensis*
Shelduck *Tadorna tadorna*
Eider *Somateria mollissima*
Long-tailed Duck *Clangula hyemalis*
Red-breasted Merganser *Mergus serrator*
Goosander *Mergus merganser*
Red Kite *Milvus milvus*
White-tailed Eagle *Haliaeetus albicilla*
Marsh Harrier *Circus aeruginosus*
Hen Harrier *Circus cyaneus*
Montagu's Harrier *Circus pygargus*
Buzzard *Buteo buteo*
Osprey *Pandion haliaetus*
Kestrel *Falco tinnunculus*
Merlin *Falco columbarius*
Peregrine *Falco peregrinus*
Corncrake *Crex crex*
Oystercatcher *Haematopus ostralegus*
Black-winged Stilt *Himantopus himantopus*
Avocet *Recurvirostra avosetta*
Little Ringed Plover *Charadrius dubius*
Ringed Plover *Charadrius hiaticula*
Kittlitz's Plover *Charadrius pecuarius*
Kentish Plover *Charadrius alexandrinus*
Lapwing *Vanellus vanellus*
Ruff *Philomachus pugnax*
godwits *Limosa* spp.
Redshank *Tringa totanus*
Wood Sandpiper *Tringa glareola*
Turnstone *Arenaria interpres*
Red-necked Phalarope *Phalaropus lobatus*
Arctic Skua *Stercorarius parasiticus*

Great Skua *Stercorarius* (syn. *Catharacta*) *skua*
White-eyed Gull *Larus leucophthalmus*
Great Black-headed Gull *Larus ichthyaetus*
Mediterranean Gull *Larus melanocephalus*
Laughing Gull *Larus atricilla*
Bonaparte's Gull *Larus philadelphia*
Black-headed Gull *Larus ridibundus*
Ring-billed Gull *Larus delawarensis*
Common Gull *Larus canus*
Lesser Black-backed Gull *Larus fuscus*
Herring Gull *Larus argentatus*
Great Black-backed Gull *Larus marinus*
Kittiwake *Rissa tridactyla*
Caspian Tern *Sterna caspia*
Royal Tern *Sterna maxima*
Lesser Crested Tern *Sterna bengalensis*
Sandwich Tern *Sterna sandvicensis*
Roseate Tern *Sterna dougallii*
Common Tern *Sterna hirundo*
Arctic Tern *Sterna paradisaea*
Forster's Tern *Sterna forsteri*
White-cheeked Tern *Sterna repressa*
Little Tern *Sterna albifrons*
Black Tern *Chlidonias niger*
skimmers *Rynchops* spp.
Guillemot *Uria aalge*
Razorbill *Alca torda*
Black Guillemot *Cepphus grylle*
Puffin *Fratercula arctica*
Spotted Wood Dove *Turtur afer*
Cuckoo *Cuculus canorus*
Snowy Owl *Nyctea scandiaca*
Kingfisher *Alcedo atthis*
African Grey Hornbill *Tockus nasutus*
Skylark *Alauda arvensis*
Swallow *Hirundo rustica*
Meadow Pipet *Anthus pratensis*
Rock Pipet *Anthus petrosus*
Wren *Troglodytes troglodytes*
Chiffchaff *Phylloscopus collybita*
Willow Warbler *Phylloscopus trochilus*
Marsh Tit *Parus palustris*
Willow Tit *Parus montanus*
treecreepers *Certhia* spp.
gonoleks *Laniarius* spp.
Carrion Crow *Corvus corone*
House Sparrow *Passer domesticus*
Chaffinch *Fringilla coelebs*
Linnet *Carduelis cannabina*

INDEX

Figures in *italics* refer to illustrations.